Acknowledgments

This publication has been made possible with the help and cooperation of many individuals and institutions. Grateful acknowledgment is made to Moore Ruble Yudell Architects & Planners, for their inspiring work and for their kind support in the preparation of this book on Moore Ruble Yudell for the AADCU Book Series of Contemporary Architects Studio Report in the United States.

AADCU Publication

www.aadcu.org
info@aadcu.org

Project Director: Bruce Q. Lan
Coordinator: Xiaoqu Luo
Curator/Editor In Chief: Bruce Q. Lan
Edited And Published By: Beijing Office, United Asia Art & Design Cooperation/bj-info@aadcu.org
In Collaboration With: Moore Ruble Yudell Architects & Planners/www.moorerubleyudell.com
d-Lab & International Architecture Research

ISBN: 978-7-5381-4946-3

编辑与出版：亚洲艺术与设计协作联盟／美国，info@aadcu.org。已授权辽宁科学技术出版社出版。
协同编辑：Moore Ruble Yudell Architects & Planners/www.moorerubleyudell.com;
国际建筑研究与设计中心／美国
主编及学术项目总策划：蓝青
协调人：罗小渠／斯坦福大学
翻　译：王韵嘉／清华大学建筑学院

Book Design:

Ken Kim, Moore Ruble Yudell + Design studio/AADCU

Authorship:

Frances Anderton: Frances Anderton is the host of *DnA: Design and Architecture*, broadcast on 89.9 KCRW in Santa Monica, California and podcast on KCRW.com. She is also the Los Angeles Editor of *Dwell* magazine and a regular contributor to *The New York Times* and other publications.

Robert Campbell: Robert Campbell, FAIA is the Pulitzer Prize winning architecture critic of *The Boston Globe* and writes a bimonthly column, "Critique," for the magazine *Architectural Record*. A graduate of Harvard College and the GSD, he has been in private practice as an architect since 1975 as a consultant to cultural institutions and cities. He has taught architectural design at several schools, most recently as Max Fisher Visiting Professor at the University of Michigan. He is a former artist-in-residence at the American Academy in Rome, and in 2004 received the annual Award of Honor of the Boston Society of Architects. With Peter Vanderwarker, he is the co-author of the book, *Cityscapes of Boston: An American City Through Time*, and his poems have been published in *The Atlantic*, *Harvard Review,* and elsewhere.

Shouzhi Wang: Born in Guangzhou, China in 1946. Professor at Art Center College of Design, Pasadena, California, USA, Vice-Dean of Changziang Design School in Shantou University, Shangou, China, Visiting Professor of Central Academy of Fine Art, Beijing and several other design schools in China. His publications include: *The History of World Modern Design*, *The History of World Graphic Design*, *The History of World Architecture*, *The History of American Illustration*, and *Planning and Design of the Commercial Residential Area*.

moore ruble yudell

architects & planners

00 CONTENTS

INTERVIEW

FRANCES ANDERTON
弗兰西斯·安德顿

访谈

Participants: Frances Anderton
Buzz Yudell
John Ruble
James Mary O'Connor

FA: This Report contains your most contemporary built and unbuilt work. What are some of its dominant themes?

BY: There are themes that have been important for us throughout our careers—30 years or so—such as: how buildings have a dialogue with the landscape, and how buildings shape spaces that are crafted for the inhabitants. But now the question is: how can we maintain these same aspirations at much denser scales, particularly in China?

In some of the recent projects, where the scale was urban, like our student center in Cincinnati or the Tango Housing project, there was a challenge of making large buildings that also developed at more intimate scales. And now in some of the work in China there's a quantum jump. In a project like in Chongqing where we have several thousand units at a very, very high density with very tall towers, how do you create a sense of community? How do you create a sense of identity for individual inhabitants and their units? How do you create a sense of neighborhood, and even what do those things mean at that scale?

FA: And how do you?

BY: Well I think it's the accumulation of a series of endeavors. First there's reading the land, and by land I

mean the urban landscape, and trying to understand how there can be a particularity about the way the buildings engage at whatever scale they're at. So even if it's towers and mid-rises they can have a strong sense of connection to that landscape in the broad sense of the word. That's one element. I think another is always thinking about designing at multiple scales so you're thinking about how either an individual or small group inhabits a space, moves through a space, how the space is choreographed.

For example, there was an apartment building we did in one of the German social housing projects where we thought very carefully about the stairway as being a place filled with light, that had a shape, that felt good when you moved through it. Then two years later we were back there for an event and this couple came up to us and asked if we could sign a book they had made called *Unser Haus* ("Our House"). They used the word house to refer to the whole apartment block with multiple units, and they had pictures of all the events that had happened and they actually talked about how that stairway had become a party space. So those multiple scales end up being very important.

Then I think another element is actually the kind of tectonics, how you scale and manipulate materials and put them together in a way that people understand how they were made, or read how they were thought about. I think Tango is one that was quite successful, where the expression of the way it was both organized geometrically and built had a lot to do with how it sat in its urban form. So there was a certain urban presence that had one scale, one palette. And then there was a sense

参与者：   弗兰西斯·安德顿（FA）
巴兹·约德（BY）
约翰·乐伯（JR）
詹姆士·马力·奥康纳（JOC）

FA：这份专集包含了你们最新的建成和未建成的项目。它的主题是什么？

BY：这些主题贯穿了我们的职业生涯，大概有30年左右，比如建筑如何与景观对话，以及建筑如何形成为居民创造的空间。但现在的问题是：我们怎样在更高的密度里延续这种理想，尤其是在中国？

我们最近的一些项目，比如在辛辛那提的学生中心或是"探戈"住宅项目中，面临的挑战是在更亲切的尺度上建造大楼。但现在在中国的一些工作是个重大的飞跃。比如在重庆的一个项目，我们要建几千个异常高密度的单元，还有很高的塔楼，那你怎么营造一种社区的感觉？你怎么为那里的居民和单元营造独特身份的感觉？你怎么营造邻里的感觉，还有这些感觉在那种尺度上意味着什么？

FA：那你们是怎么做到的？

BY：我觉得这是一系列努力的积累。首先要解读土地，这里的土地是指城市地形和景观，然后试着理解建筑在不同尺度上发挥作用的方式如何能有一种独特性。这样，即使它是塔楼或是中高层，也能与广义上的地景有很强的联系。这是一个要素。我想另一个要素是要一直考虑多重尺度上的设计，这样你就得考虑一个人或一个小团体是如何在一个空间里居住、穿行，以及这个空间是如何被精心策划设计的。

举例来说，我们在德国的一个社会住宅项目里做过一个公

6

Frances Anderton conducted this interview at the studio of Moore Ruble Yudell on August 17, 2006 in Santa Monica, California.

2006年8月17日弗兰西斯·安德顿在加利福尼亚圣莫尼卡的摩尔乐伯约德工作室主持访谈。

of discovery and a completely different set of materials that had to do with the more intimate places inside.

FA: Have you found your clients in these new countries that you're working in, receptive to your approach, especially in Asia, where one might not necessarily expect that?

JOC: What's happening in Asia is extremely competitive. They invite Californian firms to show something completely different. We offer an alternative. Some foreign firms are proposing a kind of iconic architecture that doesn't connect to local place and culture. Some developers are offering a replica version of Orange County in China. We are looking at how to connect to the ancient culture in a contemporary way, without imitating it.

FA: But how do you create a sense of place in this culture that's moving so fast and eradicating so much of what's there?

JOC: When I first went to China I thought I'd find all these exotic places and wonderful places. So much of it's gone and transformed. We're very interested in how architecture can help to preserve human memory and engage with local culture. For example, on our particular site for the project in Chongqing, there is an ancient path where people have walked for thousands of years through the city to the riverfront. We decided that it would be interesting to keep that path running through the project as a main circulation spine for the new neighborhoods that we are creating. The ancient path will take on a new life for the future.

We also discovered there's a lot of existing rock formations on the site. The Chinese people have always had a strong connection between landscape and rock. In our discussions, we pointed to the government and said, listen, this is something you can keep, it's in your history, this connection with rock. All agreed. In Chongqing, we are trying to connect the past with the future. There's a real openness there. We're only just seeing the first wave of development in China. I think it's going to get more sophisticated as time progresses.

FA: You're a firm whose work is very thoughtful. But being in China where everything's happening on such a wild scale, do you ever feel a desire to be a bit more zany? You know, do the crazy icon buildings?

JR: Well there's no question, one reason to work in a place like that is to explore things you might not be able to do at home. There's a mission to create something extraordinary, however you define that, because, again, the big scale asks for that in some ways.

Probably the most striking example of that is a competition design we've submitted to some developers in Southeast China. It's a kind of resort housing project. And this project has a scale that really exceeds anything we've ever developed, in which a series of 40-50 story buildings literally define a kind of grand garden, mostly a water garden, and in the process of doing that you create a kind of micro-environment or a micro-climate probably, that will achieve an identity through architectural design entirely. The kind of community we can make is based largely on the visual identity of the project, and then, secondly, on the opportunities for social

寓楼，我们对楼梯间进行了十分仔细的考虑，希望它充满光，有形状，从中走过的时候感觉很好。两年后我们因事回去，有一对夫妇找到我们问我们是否可以为他们制作的一本书签名，书名叫做"我们的家"。他们用"家"这个字来指代这个拥有多重单元的公寓楼街区，他们有所有在这儿发生的事件的照片，而且他们确实谈到了那个楼梯间如何成为一个聚会的场所。所以说那些多重的尺度最终被证明是十分重要的。

我想还有一个要素实际上是筑造的方式，你如何衡量、利用建筑材料并把它们融合在一起，使人们明白它们是怎么建出来的，或者解读出它们是基于什么考虑的。我觉得"探戈"住宅是一个很成功的案例，它被几何地组织并建造起来，对这个过程的表达与它在城市形态中的位置是很有关系的。所以它就有一个独特的城市外观，有一种尺度和一种色彩。然后在内部更私密的空间里，又会有一种探索的感觉，发现一套完全不同的材料。

FA：在你们工作的这些新国家中，有没有发现对你们的方法表示接受的客户？尤其是在你们可能对此期望值不高的亚洲？

JOC：在亚洲发生的事情是非常有竞争力的。他们邀请加州的事务所来展示一些完全不同的东西。我们提供了另一种选择。一些国外事务所提倡一种标志性建筑，它们与当地的地段和文化没有联系。有些开发者只是把南加州橘郡住宅模式照搬到中国。而我们则在考虑如何以一种现代的方式与古老的文化建立联系，而不是模仿。

FA：但是在这个变化如此迅速并且根除了如此多原有东西的文化中，你们怎样营造出场所感呢？

JOC：我第一次去中国的时候，我以为我会看到这些异域的、奇妙的地方。其中太多的东西都已经消失和改变了。

top left: Joseph A. Steger Student Life Center, University of Cincinnati; top right: Chun Sen Bi An Master Plan & Housing, Chongqing, People's Republic of China

左上：辛辛那提大学 Joseph A. Steger 学生生活中心
右上：中国重庆春森彼岸主平面图及住宅区

interaction in this beautiful garden of sports facilities and spas and retail shopping, and all these goodies you might say, gathered in one place.

FA: So, do you think it is possible then to create a humanistic quality at a gigantic scale?

BY: I think you've hit on the core question. We are trying to figure out what are the strategies from a design point of view by which we can start to achieve that. I think somehow in the confluence of how the landscape is shaped, how the buildings become partners with the landscape, how there's an understanding of the hierarchies of scale, how there's an understanding of community; I think those all contribute to it.

JR: In the Southeast China project though, despite the large size of the buildings, they are not simply a collection of iconic forms. They are all rather purposefully bent to the creation of this common kind of community place that they're making. Which happens to be a beautiful kind of resort atmosphere, pleasure-garden. But nevertheless, I think the sense of the humanistic comes from the fact that the buildings are more interested in the space they're creating than they are in themselves individually.

FA: Your firm has a certain set of values. Do you find that your clients overseas are seeking your values? Are you changing your values in accordance with the different places that you're working in?

BY: I think there's essentially a cross-fertilization happening and the degree to which we're being influenced

and the degree to which we are contributing fresh ideas really changes from place to place.

Just to take one example from the social housing that we've done in Germany, we won a competition there and the next day there were headlines in the newspaper—because Berlin's a place where urban design stories make the headlines, which is amazing. And one of them said "California Dream," in German, *Kalifornische Traum*, and I thought well, maybe it's just a funny tagline, but it was actually because they saw our project as being less rigid, being a little bit more improvisatory, being more connected to the land and the elements, just to take that one example. The flip side of that is that we've always been interested in social issues, having matured as students during the late 60s. We've always cared a lot about issues of housing and social housing. But in the U.S. we hadn't had a lot of opportunities to flex our muscles, whereas in Germany and Sweden, that's such an established and supported part of the culture that we got to learn a tremendous amount about how to realize affordable housing or social housing that has a lot of dignity. So I think being immersed for years in that culture brought us a tremendous amount of understanding, not just of the ideas but how you actually can make them happen in the world. So it's always some kind of cross-fertilization, which is probably why we do it, why it's exciting and I think it's important that it be a two-way dialogue.

JOC: In China we sometimes find that we're offering social values to capitalistic entrepreneurs. Our values remain humanistic at the core.

我们感兴趣的是建筑物如何帮助保存人们的记忆并参与到当地的文化之中。比如说，在我们重庆项目的地段中，有一条人们已经走了几千年的古老通道穿城而过到达河边。我们认为在这个项目中保持这条通道，使它成为一个新建的邻里间的主要流通脊梁，是很有意思的。这条古老的通道在未来将获得新的生命。

我们还在地段上发现很多原有的岩石地层。中国人一直都把地形和岩石紧密地联系在一起。我们在与政府部门讨论的时候指出了这点，跟他们说，你看，这里和岩石的关系是你们可以保持的，这是你们的历史。他们都同意了。在重庆，我们在试着联系过去和未来。那里确实有一种开放性。我们只是在见证中国的第一个发展浪潮。我相信日后它将发展得更加成熟。

FA：你们事务所的工作考虑得非常周到。但是在中国，所有事情都发生在一个狂热的尺度上，你们有没有产生过欲望，也变得滑稽异常一些，比如说做那些疯狂的标志性建筑？

JR：毫无疑问，在这个地方工作的原因之一在于这里可以探求本土不能实现的东西。我们有使命去创造一些异常的东西，无论你怎么定义它，因为，再一次说明，大的尺度从某种意义上讲需要它。

可能最显著的案例是我们向东南中国的开发商提交的一个竞赛方案。这是一个旅游度假性质的住宅项目。这个项目的尺度大大超出了我们以前开发的任何案例，在这里，一系列的40-50层大楼精确地定义了一个大公园，基本上是个水公园，在这个过程中，你可能建立一种微环境或者微气候，通过建筑设计完全地获得一种特性。我们建造的社区类型，主要取决于这个项目的视觉特性，其次取决于在这个体育设施、温泉疗养、零售商业以及这些所有有趣的东西聚集在一起的漂亮公园里发生的社交互动。

top left: Resort Development, South East Asia; top right: Workshop for Karow Nord Master Plan, Berlin, Germany

左上：东南中国旅游度假开发区
右上：德国柏林 Karow Nord 总体规划的工作间现场

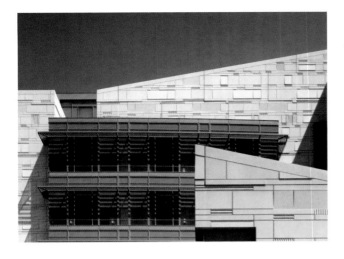

FA: And I'm also hearing that you're the humanists. Humanism used to be associated with Europeans. And now it's you that's bringing context to these old cultures. Doesn't it seem odd to be coming from California and telling people how to respect their heritage?

JR: But I think that's probably because the whole experience of living in North America is one of course of trying to manifest culture in a huge landscape where there isn't a human culture already, at least not the European kind. So I think we're much more oriented in the United States to preserving, creating, making places, trying to bring things together, trying to create some sense of urban place, although that's of course very contradictory because of all the highways we have in Los Angeles and so forth. But I do think that we want to make places, we want to reinforce places. We don't want to just create an architectural counterpoint to an historic context.

FA: And let's, since you've just mentioned North America, talk a bit about your projects here.

JR: Well we have generally been known here for our work in universities and institutional buildings, and we've done some work recently that we're very proud of in those areas. The Santa Monica Public Library, the Fresno Courthouse, some beautiful work at UCLA for Glorya Kaufman Hall, which was a very sensitive remodeling and reworking of an historic building. And I think that our work does show the full range of what we do, albeit it doesn't go into some of the extremes that we have gone into in Europe or Asia in terms of scale. But I think the opportunities to work close to home where we can take the work through all phases and do construc-

tion documents is very important to us and we ardently seek work in California.

FA: Does that mean you can't take your work through all the construction phases in some of your projects overseas?

JR: It's a different process and you know it's going to be somewhat more at arm's length so that is going to be a challenge.

FA: But your firm's work is known for its attention to detail and the really strong resolution of the ideas. Is it frustrating to be limited in that way?

JOC: Well, we have different kinds of collaborations in different countries. Like say in Sweden for the Tango project or the Potatisåkern project, you're taking two very good firms, SWECO and FFNS, that we worked with locally in Malmö, and ourselves. Putting the two together you're getting something very powerful, a high level of architecture. In China it's quite different. Coming from the old system they have the institutes that originally grew out of the university system. But there are all kinds of levels of ability. We'd never get involved in a process where we would hand over the drawings and say here you are, we've finished our design, good luck. We have to have it so that we're involved all the way through construction.

But it's hard. In Tianjin, which includes ten thousand units of housing in all, I remember a scene during one of our trips there for meetings. The Client wanted us to do the final review for all of the Construction Documents

ＦＡ：那么，你们认为有可能在一个巨大的尺度上营造人性的特质吗？

ＢＹ：我觉得你提出了最关键的问题。我们正在试着找出可以达到这个目的的设计策略。我觉得这应该是几个问题的综合，比如地形是怎么形成的，建筑怎么与地形相协调，对尺度的层次怎么理解，对社区怎么理解等，这些都能解释这个问题。

ＪＲ：在东南中国项目中，建筑尽管体量很大，却并不是简单的地标形式的汇集，它们都有意地屈从于它们所营造的这个普通社区，这个具有度假气息的漂亮乐园。但是，我认为人性的意义体现在这些建筑对于它们营造的空间，这比他们单独的本身更有兴趣。

ＦＡ：你们的事务所有一套特殊的评判标准。你们觉得你们的海外客户是在寻求你们的标准吗？你们有没有为了和不同的工作地点取得一致而改变你们的标准？

ＢＹ：我认为本质上是个互相交流的过程，我们受到影响的程度和我们贡献新想法的程度，在每个地方都是不一样的。

就拿我们在德国做的社会住宅来说，我们在竞赛中得了奖，第二天就上了报纸头条——因为在柏林，一个城市设计的故事就可以当头条，这很令人惊讶。其中一篇文章说到"加州梦想"，我就想，这可能只是个有趣的标签，但实际上是因为他们觉得我们的方案不那么死板，即兴的东西多一些，并且和土地及各种元素联系更紧密一些。从另一方面看这件事，由于我们成长于20世纪60年代，那时是我们的学生时代，一直都对社会问题感兴趣，而且一直很关注住宅和社会住宅的问题。但是在美国，我们没有太多机会施展才能，而在德国和瑞典则相反，这是他们文化中确定的并受到支持的一部分，所以我们要学很多，关于如

top left: United States Courthouse, Fresno, California; center: Glorya Kaufman Hall, University of California, Los Angeles; top right: Tango, Bo01 Housing Exhibition, Malmö, Sweden

左上：加利福尼亚弗雷斯诺美国联邦法院大楼；
中间：洛杉矶加州大学的Glorya Kaufman礼堂；
右上：瑞典马尔默"探戈"Bo01住宅博览会

for the first phase, which is about 1,500 housing units. They decided that they couldn't send these construction drawings over to our offices in Santa Monica for review, because that process would take too long and they needed them right away. So they almost locked us up in a room for a week, with three architectural institutes, and 20 architects, lining up with sets of drawings, and told us, please correct them. Halil Dolan, Akai Yang and I would review the drawings, mark and redline them up, and they would come back the next day with the revised drawings for us to review again, and so on. Everything had to be done on the spot and it was an exhausting week of review and coordination.

FA: There are some issues that are common to architects in general, at present: sustainability, for example, large scale, densification of cities, materials, and the digital revolution. How are those factors affecting the—I don't want to use the word style—aesthetic approach in your work?

BY: Well, I'll just use one example of a project where we're having the opportunity to study those issues very carefully, which is the new Sloan School of Business for MIT, just now in Schematic Design. MIT is an interesting place because for a number of years, as you know, they have raised their aspirations about architecture and planning, with people like Bill Mitchell and others on campus. And now they're raising the level of ambition about what we loosely call Integrated Building Systems, which means thinking about the building very, very thoroughly from the beginning as an integration of a series of systems and materials and how that affects sustainability, affects performance, affects the experi-

ence of it, including all the systems, mechanical, electrical, plumbing, structural, landscape. We have this fellow, Marc Rosenbaum, who's one of the great sustainability consultants and is a spectacular consultant for all the mechanical systems. So in the end the building may not shout that this building is about sustainability, but it will be woven into the fabric of the building.

I think another one that has been quite interesting recently is the University of Cincinnati. They've been very ambitious with their architectural program, and having done a Frank Gehry building and an Eisenman and a whole series of adventurous buildings, they were at a point where they said we have wonderful new buildings but they're all icons. How do we make a place where the public spaces are at least as important as the buildings? And they brought in Thom Mayne and us and Charles Gwathmey and George Hargreaves.

The primary issue was how to shape community, and I think what was really fascinating there was to see three very strong buildings come out of it, and if you pulled each one out they could be iconic but your experience of it, even with Thom's building which is very dramatic and very beautiful sculpturally, is that you don't walk through and say, oh, there's a Morphosis icon, there's a Gwathmey icon. You walk through and you experience different kinds of community, different scales of opportunity, different sort of rhythms of how this, the campus heart, functions. It's been a chance to integrate these timeless humanistic principles with new and evolving ways of building.
JOC: You mentioned the digital revolution. Well, the older Santa Monica Library was always a quiet kind of place where people would go and you'd keep quiet.

何建造人们支付得起的，同时又有尊贵地位的住宅或社会住宅。所以我认为，在这样的文化中被浸染多年，不仅大大加深了我们对这种概念的理解，也让我们学会如何让这种概念在全世界实现。所以这通常都是一种互相交流，可能这就是我们为什么这么做，为什么它这么令人振奋的缘由。我认为双方面的对话是很重要的。

JOC：在中国，我们有时发觉自己在为资本企业家提供社会价值。我们的价值在核心上依然是人性的。

FA：我还听说你们是人性主义者。人性主义以前都是和欧洲人联系在一起的。而现在是你们给这些古老文化带来文脉。你们来自加州，告诉人们如何尊重他们的遗产，这不会感觉很怪吗？

JR：但我认为，这可能是因为在北美生活的整个经历就是要在一个巨大的地形上试图表现出文化，那里原来并没有人类文化，至少不是欧洲那种。所以在美国，我们更多地在保护、创造和营建空间，试图融会贯通，试图营造出城市空间的感觉，当然这也是矛盾的地方，因为在洛杉矶等地方有大量高速路。但我确信我们是想营建空间，加强空间。我们不想只是在历史文脉里建立一个对应的建筑物。

FA：既然你刚刚提到北美，就来谈谈你在这儿的项目吧。

JR：我们在这里基本上以大学和公共机构建筑而出名，最近我们也在这些领域做了些我们很引以为傲的作品。像圣莫尼卡公立图书馆、弗雷斯诺法院，还有在UCLA的漂亮的Glorya Kaufman礼堂，这是对一个历史建筑非常敏感的重塑和改造。我认为我们的作品显示了我们工作的全部范畴，尽管我们没有像在欧洲和亚洲那样在尺度上走到极端。但我想在家的附近工作，我们可以经历一个项目的各个阶段并绘制施工文件，这个机会是非常重要的，而

above: View of Main Street with the Student Recreation Center (Morphosis), Student Center (Gwathmey-Siegel), and the Student Life Center at the University of Cincinnati

上图：主街上的学生娱乐中心(Morphosis)，学生中心(Gwathmey-Siegel)以及辛辛那提大学学生生活中心的景观图

Today kids are so used to a very interactive environment, downloading, iPoding, IMing, e-mailing each other, checking myspace, it's a very different kind of place. When we go to the library now, it's more of a meeting place, a room for interaction, a kind of community. That's kind of an exciting time for a building. Many people thought the library would actually disappear with new technology. In fact what's happening is that it is actually transforming it.

FA: Can you single out any other projects that are in some way pivotal for the firm?

JR: Well, I do feel the Santa Monica Library works that way. It's not entirely new in the sense of physical form, but for us I think it represents a very high level of bringing so many different considerations together.

We pride ourselves on being multi-valent, or building places that are kind of organic in the sense that they address many different considerations at once. Our work is not just about form. It's not just about cultural shock, or maybe it isn't at all about cultural shock. But it's definitely about creating whole places that have many attributes and I think the Library is a good example of that because I would say there is nothing in the building that is not in some way purposeful. We're striving for a Gold or at least a Silver LEED certification so it has many sustainable features, but I think above all, our hope is that it will turn out to be socially or culturally sustainable in the sense that people will care for it. And that's one of the things we're proudest of, that we've created places that people identify with so strongly and care about that they actually maintain them and invest a great deal in them

in that sense. That is what I think of as a kind of cultural sustainability, which I think, is extremely important.

JOC: A new project that we're doing is the Santa Monica Parking Structure. After we came back from Sweden, where we were learning a lot about sustainability, we were looking for projects in which we could use some of that, and along comes a project like Santa Monica Parking. You don't normally think of architecture when you think of a parking structure.

This one is a parking structure for 900 cars, right in the Civic Center, which will help to create a new gateway to the Civic Center. We talked to the City Client and asked if we could use this opportunity to design a sustainable parking structure. The City had just written their new sustainable green standards and we thought that the Parking Structure might reflect these newly developed standards. The roof will be clad in photovoltaic panels and this will shade the cars while generating electricity. The street level will have public uses; there will be a café at Civic Center Drive. The glass panels with different colors on the exteriors will harvest light into the structure, reduce the apparent scale of the building, and add a sense of syncopated movement to the building.

I think it'll be one of the first sustainable parking structures in the country. It extends architecture to the ordinary buildings that make up our cities.

FA: You say the parking structure was inspired by lessons learned in Sweden. What else have you brought back into the office from your overseas experiences?

且我们热切地寻找加州的项目。

FA：你是说在国外的一些项目中你们的工作没有贯穿整个施工阶段？

JR：那是一个不同的过程，而且你知道那个过程比较难接触到，所以这会是个挑战。

FA：但是你们事务所的工作是以对细节的关注和对概念的坚定决心而出名的。面对这样的限制没有挫败感吗？

JOC：在不同的国家我们有不同方式的合作。比如说在瑞典的"探戈"项目和Potatisåkern项目中，我们和两家非常好的公司——SWECO和FFNS合作，后者我们曾在马尔默合作过。两者合在一起，就能产生非常强大的力量及高水平的建筑。在中国就完全不同。由于旧体制的缘故，他们有大学系统里发展出来的机构。但是能力却千差万别。我们不会参与这样的项目：我们把图纸交上去说，给你，我们的设计完成了，祝你好运。我们必须拥有图纸，参与到施工的所有环节。

但这很难。在天津，有个项目共包含一万个住宅单元，我还记得我们有一次去开会的情景。客户想让我们对一期的施工图纸做最后的检查，那大概是1500个住宅单元。他们觉得他们不能把这些施工图送到我们在圣莫尼卡的办公室去检查，因为那个过程太花时间，而他们马上要这些文件。于是他们几乎是把我们锁在一个屋子里一个星期，一同的还有其他三个建筑机构的20多位建筑师以及一套套的施工图，并告诉我们，请把图纸改好。Halil Dolan，Akai Yang和我检查图纸，用红笔作下修改记号，然后他们第二天再拿着修改过的图纸来让我们再次检查，以此类推。所有工作都在现场完成，那真是劳累的检查和合作的一周。

FA：有一些问题对现在的建筑师来说是具有普遍性的：

above: Santa Monica Public Library, Santa Monica, California　　　上图：加州圣莫尼卡的公共图书馆　　　**11**

JR: We're just about to have an exhibition early next year in the Santa Monica Library about Nordic modernism, mainly furniture and lighting design of the early post-war period into the current time, and also showing its influence on the design of the Library. So in one sense our experience in Sweden and Scandinavia has worked its way on us in terms of really developing a very, very strong feeling about that functional but beautiful approach to architecture and design.

FA: And James you've spent a lot of time in China. Does anything stand out that you've brought back or has changed you as an architect?

JOC: Working in China has really stretched me as an architect and as a human being. It has exerted incredibly high personal demands on me. China is certainly the future and it's certainly going through dramatic change. I think it's very early on in terms of where it's going to end up. I like to think that on our projects over there, we are bringing a sense of hope for the future.

FA: What do you think Charles Moore would have to say about Moore Ruble Yudell, 2007?

BY: Charles loved nothing better than interacting with other cultures and bringing back pieces of them and cross-fertilizing from culture to culture. So I think he would be excited about the interchange, the change that you experience in different cultures and the kind of energy that brings.

比如说可持续性、大型尺度、城市的高密度化、材料，还有数码的进步。这些因素是怎么影响你们作品的——我不想用"风格"这个词——那么美学手法呢？

BY：我就用MIT的新斯隆商学院来举例吧。方案现在还处于概念设计阶段，在这个项目里我们就有机会十分仔细地研究这些问题。MIT是一个很有意思的地方，因为有几年，你知道，像Bill Mitchell以及其他一些人在校的时候，他们掀起了一股建筑和规划的浪潮。而现在，他们又提出了我们姑且称为"综合建筑系统"的野心，这是指从一开始就非常非常彻底地把建筑看作一系列系统和材料的综合体，并考虑它如何影响可持续性、人的行为、人对它的体验，以及所有的系统：机械、电力、水暖、结构和景观。我们这儿有一个人Marc Rosenbaum，他是最出色的可持续性的顾问之一，同时也是所有机械系统的杰出顾问。所以最后这个建筑可能没有对外宣称它是可持续的，但这一点已与建筑交织在一起。

我认为最近在辛辛那提大学的例子也很有趣。他们一直在他们的建筑项目上很有野心，在做了一个Frank Gehry大楼、一个Eisenman大楼还有整整一系列的冒险性建筑之后，他们现在的处境是，就像他们自己说的，"我们有很棒的建筑，但他们都是标志性的。我们如何营造一个地段，使那里的公共空间至少和那里的建筑一样重要？"然后，他们就找到Thom Mayne、Charles Gwathmey、George Hargreaves和我们。

最重要的问题是如何形成社区，我觉得吸引人的是：看到三幢非常强势的建筑拔地而起，你把其中哪一个单独拉出来，它都是标志性的，但你对它的体验并不是从中穿过然后说，噢，那有个Morphosis标志，这有个Gwathmey标志，即使对Thom的非常戏剧化、有雕塑感的建筑来说也是一样。你从中穿过，体验到的是不同种类的社区、不同尺度的机遇，还有这个校园的心脏发挥其作用的

不同节奏。这是一个把这些永恒的人性原则与新的、不断发展的建筑方式结合起来的机会。

JOC：你提到了数码的进步。原先的圣莫尼卡图书馆一直是个安静的地方，人们去那里的时候，要保持安静。但现在孩子们已经习惯于有很强互动性的场所，他们在那里下载，用iPod、IM，给对方发邮件，查看个人空间等，这是一个完全不同类型的地方。现在如果我们去图书馆，那里就更多地成为一个会面的场所，一个互动的空间，一种社区。这对一幢建筑来说是激动人心的。很多人原以为图书馆会因为新技术而消失。实际上，新技术正在对它进行改造。

FA：你们能挑选出几个对你们的公司来说起到关键作用的项目吗？

JR：我确实觉得圣莫尼卡图书馆就是一例。从物质形态的角度来说它并不是全新的，但是我认为它是把许多不同的考虑放在一起的高水平体现。

我们是"多价"的，或者说我们在营造的空间是有机的，因为它们同时表达了许多不同的考虑，我们很为此自豪。我们的设计不只是关于形式的。它也不只是关于文化震撼，或者说可能它与文化震撼根本无关。但它肯定与营造具有多重性质的整体空间有关，我认为这个图书馆就是这样一个绝佳的案例，因为从某种角度讲，我可以说在这幢建筑里所有东西都是有目的的。我们在为获得LEED证明的金奖，或至少银奖而努力，所以这个建筑有很多可持续性的特征，但我想最重要的是，我们希望它最后成为社会上或文化上可持续的，即人们会对它加以关注。而这正是我们最自豪的事情之一，我们创造出来的空间得到人们强烈的认同和关注，他们继而保持着这些空间，在其中投入很多。我觉得这就是一种文化的持续性，我认为它是极其重要的。

above: Santa Monica Parking Structure, Santa Monica, California

上图：加州圣莫尼卡停车场

JOC：我们在做的一个新项目是圣莫尼卡停车场。在瑞典我们学了很多可持续性方面的东西，回来后我们就在寻找可以用的上这些东西的项目，这时我们遇到了圣莫尼卡停车场这个项目。当你想到停车场的时候，你一般不会想到建筑学。

这是一个可容纳900辆车的停车场，就在市民中心里面，它将帮助塑造一个新的中心大门。我们问我们的城市客户，我们可不可以利用这个机会设计一个可持续性的停车场建筑。市里刚编订了新的可持续绿色标准，我们觉得这个停车场可以反映这些新标准。屋顶上将覆有光电板，发电的时候可为汽车遮阴。街道平面层将具有公共用途，在市民中心的车道上将有一个咖啡厅。外表面上各种颜色的玻璃板将把光线收集到这个设备里来，减小建筑的外显体量，并给建筑加上一个切分的节奏。

我认为这将是全国第一个可持续性的停车场。它将建筑学扩展到那些构成了我们的城市的普通建筑。

FA：你说这个停车场的灵感来自于瑞典的课程。你们公司还借鉴了哪些在海外经历中的优秀经验？

JR：我们正准备明年初在圣莫尼卡图书馆举行一个关于北欧现代主义的展览，主要是战后早期至今的家具和灯具设计，同时也展示它对我们这个图书馆设计的影响。所以从某种意义上来说，我们在瑞典和斯堪的纳维亚半岛的经历对我们的影响体现在，让我们对既注重功能又很漂亮的建筑和设计的方法萌生了非常强烈的感情。

FA：詹姆士，你在中国工作了很长的时间。有没有什么很突出的东西，你把它带了回来，或者它改变了作为建筑师的你？

JOC：在中国的工作确实使我作为一个建筑师同时也作为一个人的视野得到了拓展。它给我提出了非常高的个人要求。中国无疑是属于未来的，它现在无疑正在经历着戏剧性的变化。我觉得现在说它最终会是什么样还为时尚早。我愿意相信，通过我们在那儿的项目，我们带去了对未来的希望。

FA：你们觉得查尔斯·摩尔会对2007年的MRY说些什么？

BY：查尔斯最喜欢与其他文化互动，带回它们的片段，让文化与文化互相交流。所以我想他会对在不同文化中经历到的交互以及它所带来的能量感到兴奋。

MAKING PLACE

ROBERT CAMPBELL, FAIA
罗伯特 · 坎贝尔, AIA院士

地域营建

My first serious contact with Moore Ruble Yudell occurred in Washington in 1996. I'd long been acquainted with the firm's senior partner, the celebrated architect Charles W. Moore, but Moore had died three years earlier. John Ruble and Buzz Yudell were in Washington to present their proposed design for a new American Embassy in Berlin. They were one of six firms, all nationally known, that the State Department had asked to prepare a design for a critical site next to the Brandenburg Gate. I was a member of the jury that was to pick the best design and recommend it to the government.

Without a dissenting vote, we picked Moore Ruble Yudell's. Their building was by far the most intelligently organized and by far the most thoughtfully worked out in detail. But beyond that, it embodied, in ways I won't try to describe in words, metaphors of American life and culture. It was a building that people would enjoy inhabiting, partying in, working in. It was respectful of its historic surroundings without losing its sense of its own individuality. It was the kind of building we too rarely see today.

We live in an era when the world of architecture is split into two camps. There are the famous avant-garde architects, who dominate the press with a few buildings of spectacular novelty, buildings that become personal expressions of the architect's talent and often bring him or her celebrity. The most notable to date is probably the Guggenheim Museum in Bilbao, Spain, by the American architect Frank O. Gehry. These are often wonderful buildings, and people rightly travel long distances to see them. But at the same time, few people want their own house or school or workplace to be de-

signed in a similar style. They resent the rupture with a familiar language of architecture they have learned to appreciate. The avant-garde work feels arbitrary to them, without discernible meaning. That fact leads people to believe that architects possess an entirely different aesthetic from their own. As a result, they begin to distrust contemporary architects and architecture. They then fall back into the opposite camp. They become reactionaries, who demand buildings in familiar historic styles. Such buildings, when actually built, nearly always turn out to be pathetically weak imitations of what were once vital traditions.

Meanwhile, fear of the new leads to an exaggerated desire for the preservation of whatever is old. At times it seems as if the preservation movement and the environmental movement are the only non-economic values that our society now perceives in architecture. That being so, it's hard to persuade clients to pay for good new architecture, because nobody agrees on what good architecture is.

What makes Moore Ruble Yudell important in this situation is that, more than almost any other architects, they are in the business of bridging the gap between the avant-garde and the reactionary. They make buildings that remember the familiar language of architecture, its roofs and windows and materials, its human scale, its wish to be inhabited, and its respect for context, both cultural and physical. They employ a known visual language which, like all languages, is largely made up of conventions. But like good writers who work with a verbal language, they don't simply repeat the past. They never fail to innovate. Sometimes they do this to address

我与MRY的第一次正式接触始于1996年的华盛顿。之前我与事务所长年的合伙人，著名建筑师查尔斯·摩尔（Charles W. Moore）熟识，但此时他已经去世3年了。当时约翰·乐伯（John Ruble）和巴兹·约德（Buzz Yudell）在华盛顿为新的美国驻柏林大使馆方案作介绍。当时共有六家国内知名的事务所受国务院之邀，在伯兰登堡城门旁的一个苛刻的地段上做一个方案。我是评审团成员之一，需要挑选出一个最好的方案并把它推荐给政府。

我们全票通过并选中了MRY的方案。他们的建筑是所有方案里组织最巧妙的，也是细节设计最周到的。但除此之外，它还以不可言喻的方式表达了对美国生活与文化的隐喻。这是一幢人们将乐意在其中居住、聚会和工作的建筑。它尊重其周围的历史环境，同时保有独特的个性。这种建筑在现在已经太少见了。

在我们这个时代里，建筑界分为两大阵营。一种是著名的先锋派建筑师，凭借几幢引人入胜的新奇建筑掌控着媒体，这些建筑成为建筑师才华的个性表达，通常为他们带来名誉。可追溯的最著名的例子应该是美国建筑师弗兰克·盖里（Frank O. Gehry）在西班牙毕尔巴鄂建造的古根海姆博物馆。它们通常是令人惊奇的建筑，人们理所当然地长途旅行去瞻仰它们。但同时，很少有人希望它们自己的家、学校或工作场所被设计成同样风格。他们憎恨与他们已学会欣赏的熟悉的建筑语言之间的割裂。先锋派的作品让他们觉得是专断的而且意义不明，这个事实让人们觉得建筑师和他们的审美观完全不同。结果，人们开始对当代的建筑师和建筑失去信任。于是他们掉头回到另一个阵营。他们成为保守派，希望建筑成为熟悉的古典式样。而当这样的建筑实际建成，它们几乎无一例外地成为对曾经辉煌的传统的可怜且无力的模仿。

同时，对新事物的惧怕导致了一种对所有古老事物进行保

14

circumstances that are new, such as the need in our time to create buildings that are less exploitive of the planet's resources. But at other times they innovate for the sheer joy of invention and surprise—the unexpected gesture that makes a place different and memorable.

Such gestures are important in any art. But they can only be meaningful when they occur against the background of some framework of expectation. The poet Robert Frost once famously said that, for him, writing free verse would be like playing tennis without a net. How would he know when he'd made a good shot? He needed the framework of rhyme and meter, as the tennis player needs a court and a net and a book of rules. Moore Ruble Yudell are architects in the manner that Frost was a poet. You're always aware of the architectural parentage of their buildings, the known typologies developed over time, the court and the book of rules. It's against that background that you can read and enjoy their innovations, as they explore, with keen attention, everything that is novel or particular about the circumstance in which the building finds itself—circumstance of site, function, users, culture, construction, symbolic message. They make this point explicitly in their praise of the Portuguese architect Alvaro Siza: "His elemental forms connect to traditional ways of building...and still delight us with their fresh expression."

The Spanish architect Jose Rafael Moneo, architect of the new Los Angeles Cathedral, is another architect who, like Moore Ruble Yudell, seeks to close the gap between the public and the avant-garde. He speaks of "the importance of a shared language that might go some way to overcoming the wild individualism of to-

day," and in another essay he writes: "The only sensation of reality left for architecture today resides in its history. The world of images provided by history is the only sensible reality that has not been destroyed by scientific knowledge or by society."

Reading the texts by John Ruble and Buzz Yudell for this book, we're struck by the prevalence of gerunds, nouns that end in "-ing" and speak of process, of things still in a state of becoming, rather than of conclusions or products. We read of "shaping, sculpting, gathering, dividing, making, crafting, ordering, manifesting," and many others. It's a way of thinking and writing that ties the firm back to another kind of history, the life of the firm's mentor, Charles Moore. Moore wrote a classic book (with Donlyn Lyndon and Gerald Allen) called *The Place of Houses* that is also filled with gerunds: "enfronting," "inhabiting," many more. Moore's buildings always gave you the sense of being in a state of inquiry and exploration, as if they were on the way to finding their final form but hadn't quite got there yet. It's a manner of design that accepts the inhabitant, and what the inhabitant will do to the building, as an equal partner in the design process. Such buildings seem to welcome their future users with open arms. Unlike the work of high-style architects who present you with a finished aesthetic whole, in which you will always feel yourself to be a visitor or even an intruder, the works of Moore, and of Moore Ruble Yudell, seek to be completed by human habitation. Often, indeed, the future inhabitant is engaged much earlier on, as a literal participant in the design process. Like Charles Moore, Ruble and Yudell like to lead charrettes, intense, short creative sessions in which all the people involved in a future building—

护的夸张欲望。有时，看起来似乎我们的社会从建筑感知到的唯一非经济价值就是保护运动和环境运动。如此一来，客户们很难愿意为好的新建筑投资，因为人们已经不知道什么是好的建筑。

在这种情况下，MRY之所以变得重要，是因为他们和几乎其他任何建筑师相比，都更注重连接先锋派与保守派之间的空隙。他们的建筑拥有对建筑的熟悉语言的回忆，其屋顶、窗户和材料，其人性的尺度，它对居住的渴望以及它对文脉的文化、物质双方面的尊重。他们运用的已知视觉语言，像所有语言一样，是由惯例形成的。但是和使用自然语言的作家一样，他们并不是简单地重复过去。他们从来没有忘记创新。有时他们创新是为了处理新的情况，比如我们这个时代需要对地球资源开发较少的建筑。但更多的时候他们创新只是为了享受创造和惊奇所带来的纯粹快感——一个出乎意料的表达使一个地段变得不同而难忘。

这样的表达在任何艺术中都有重要的地位。但是它们只有当在一个预期的框架背景中出现的时候才有意义。诗人罗伯特·弗罗斯特（Robert Frost）曾说过，对他来说，写自由体诗就像打没有网的网球。他怎么知道自己何时出彩？他需要韵脚和格律的框架，就像网球运动员需要场地、网和规则。MRY作为建筑师就像弗罗斯特作为诗人那样。你总是可以看出他们楼房的建筑学源头，看出发展过的已知原型，看出场地和规则。正是在这种背景之上，你可以看出并欣赏他们的创新，他们拥有敏锐的注意力，在建筑的具体情况（即场地、功能、使用者、文化、构造、符号信息等情况）中探索一切新鲜、奇特的事物。在对葡萄牙建筑师阿尔瓦罗·西扎（Alvaro Siza）的赞美中，他们明确地表达了这一点："他将基本形式和传统的建筑方式联系在一起，然而仍然以它们鲜活的表达使我们感到愉悦。"

洛杉矶大教堂的设计者西班牙建筑师胡塞·拉塞尔·莫奈

sometimes including members of the general public, who after all will have to live with it—work together to generate ideas and discern shared values.

A visit to the Moore Ruble Yudell office in Santa Monica, at this moment of the firm's life, is a visual delight and a metaphor for its architecture. As you open the door you have a straight visual shot through the office to an idyllic California courtyard beyond, a view that is terminated by the far courtyard wall, painted an intense shade of red-orange selected by Tina Beebe, who specializes in color and materials and who gives the firm's work much of its panache. The wall rises as a complementary color above a stand of blue-green agave plants. As you move toward this courtyard, drawn as if by a kind of tropism, you become aware that you are passing through a former industrial loft, with sunlight drifting through bowstring trusses from skylights overhead. The office is, thus, fresh wine in an old bottle, taking advantage of the surprise and pleasure of the juxtaposition in every possible way, much as the firm's new buildings play with the relationships of memory and invention.

"Creation Is a Patient Search," wrote the great architect Le Corbusier in the title of one of his books. John Ruble, Buzz Yudell and their associates are still engaged in a lifelong search, and the work is still evolving. Recent projects seem calmer and crisper than in the past, more confident, less theatrical, and less dependent on literal references to historic styles. Now 55, the partners are, in all likelihood, entering on the best years of their practice.

欧(Jose Rafael Moneo)和MRY一样在努力弥合大众与先锋派之间的缝隙。他谈到"可能对战胜现今泛滥的个人主义有点用处的一种共享语言的重要性",而在另一篇文章中他写道:"现在留给建筑师的唯一现实感知存在于历史之中。由历史提供的图像世界,是还未被科学知识或社会摧毁的唯一可感知的现实。"

在读到约翰·乐伯和巴兹·约德为本书写的文字时,我们震惊地看到频繁使用的动名词和名词,它们以"正在进行的时态"开头,表示着过程本身以及仍在变化状态中的事物,而不是结论或成果。我们读到"正在形成、正在塑造、正在聚集、正在分裂、正在营建、正在制作、正在指定、正在出现"等。这种思考和写作的方式将事务所与另一段历史——事务所的导师,查尔斯·摩尔的一生都联系在一起。摩尔和唐林·林登(Donlyn Lyndon)以及杰拉德·艾伦(Gerald Allen)写了一本经典著作《住宅场所》,其中也是充满了动名词:正在遇到、正在居住等。摩尔的建筑总给你一种在询问和探索的状态中的感觉,就像它们正在寻找它们的最后形式,但还没完全到达终点。这种设计方式使房子的居住者以及他们在房子中做的事情成为设计过程的一部分。这种建筑就像伸开双臂迎接着它们未来的使用者一样。高调的建筑师总是为你呈现一个已完成的美学整体,在其中你总是感觉自己是个访客或甚至是个入侵者。与他们不同,摩尔和MRY的作品,需要人的居住使其变得完整。确实,未来的居住者经常早早地就参与进来,成为设计过程中名副其实的一部分。比如查尔斯·摩尔,乐伯以及约德喜欢举行激烈、简短、充满创造性的小型研讨会,在会上所有参与将来建设的人——有时包括最终要和建筑相处的普通大众——一起产生想法并辨明共同目标。

在现在这个时刻,对MRY事务所在圣莫尼卡的办公室的造访是一种视觉上的享受,同时,也是对其建筑的一种隐喻。一打开门,你的目光将穿过办公室,直射到后面的一个田园风光的加州庭院,目光的终端是庭院的一面墙,它由热烈的橘红色粉刷,这个颜色是蒂娜·毕比(Tina Beebe)挑选的,她对颜色和材料有特殊研究,为事务所的作品加以润色。这面墙形成了一丛蓝绿色龙舌兰的补色。当你像被吸引着一样走近这个庭院的时候,你意识到自己是在一个从前的工业时代阁楼里穿行,天窗中的阳光穿过钢索构架倾泻而下。如此,整个办公室就是古老酒瓶里的鲜酿,它利用了各种可能的并置所带来的惊喜与愉悦,正如同事务所在其新作品中对回忆和创新的关系的把玩。

"创造就是耐心地寻找。"伟大的建筑师柯布西耶在他一本书的标题中这样写道。约翰·乐伯,巴斯·约德以及他们的合伙人仍在用他们的毕生寻找,他们的作品仍在演进。最近的项目比以前的更加冷静、清新,更加自信,不再像以前那么戏剧化,也不再那么依赖对历史风格的表面附会。他们都正当55岁的年龄,这也很可能是进入他们实践的最佳时代。

Reprinted with permission from *Moore Ruble Yudell: Making Place* (Mulgrave, Australia: Images Publishing Group, 2004)

由摩尔乐伯约德授权许可翻印: *Making Place* (澳大利亚 Mulgrave 图像出版社,2004年)

United States Embassy, Berlin, Germany: Opposite the Tiergarten
the Embassy rooftop is mounted by a penthouse—a house of State
whose focal point is the glassy conference room of the Lantern.

德国柏林的美国大使馆：对面是Tiergarten，
使馆屋顶建有阁楼公寓，
楼顶玻璃会议室的穹顶塔成为建筑的焦点

01 FITTING IN

LIVING SUSTAINABLY ON THE LAND

适应　居住地的可持续性生活

可持续性建筑始于对使场所营建变得独特并重要的那些力量和性质的理解。对一个场所的气候、景观和环境的生态关系的理解，使我们可以开始与场所对话。最具可持续性的建筑是从对建筑项目及其地理位置的考虑开始的。这些基本的考虑反过来又导致了一系列连续统一的决定，从规划到系统整合再到材料选择。最终，建筑、景观和居民们互相影响，并为彼此带来意义。可持续性建筑不仅使资源的使用最优化，还帮助维系并更新着我们的文化与精神。

Sustainable building begins with the understanding of the forces and qualities that make places unique and vital. Understanding the ecology of climate, landscape, and habitation of a place allows us to begin a dialogue with that place. The most sustainable architecture begins with the thoughtful consideration of the building program and site. These fundamental decisions in turn inform a continuum of decisions from planning to systems integration to material selection. Ultimately, the building, landscape, and inhabitants interact and bring meaning to one another. Sustainable buildings are places which not only optimize the use of resources, but which help to sustain and renew our culture and spirit.

YUDELL/BEEBE HOUSE

约德/毕比住宅

This house developed in close response to the rhythms and materials of the rugged coast of Northern California. Close to a coastal bluff, the site falls under strict architectural guidelines. We sought to embrace the fundamental environmental intentions of the guidelines while creating a contemporary place of strong individual character and quiet complexity.

LIVING IN THE LAND
Each part of the house responds to its specific site conditions. The east elevation presents a rugged entry, a contemporary interpretation of the "western front." The south opens to the ocean with full or partial shading. The west screens the interior from houses across the meadow while framing water and rocks through habitable bays. The north is shaped as an intimate court with mountain views. A garden of native grasses and rocks suggests the connection of mountain to ocean. The movement and transparency through the heart of the house complete this spatial link.

MOVING THROUGH LIGHT AND SPACE
Movement through and around the house is choreographed to enhance the spatial and sensate experience. Spaces are shaped simply in plan, yet shift dramatically in height and present a layered sequence of framed views and paths. The building form and exterior spaces define each other in dynamic dialogue.

Windows are composed to frame near and distant landscapes and to celebrate the movement and wash of light. The northeast-facing courtyard catches the morning sun and screens prevailing winds. The towers of the studios collect light and enhance convection. They are markers in the landscape while meeting the sixteen-foot height limit. The house is configured as a one-room deep array so that all spaces have multiple exposures, optimizing daylight and ventilation.

In harmony with its environment, the house celebrates craft and materials and shapes a retreat for quiet contemplation or spirited social interaction.

这幢住宅的设计对加州北部崎岖不平的海岸的节奏与材质做出了巧妙的应答。地段紧邻一面海滨悬崖，因此受到严格的建筑方面的限制。我们试图在遵守这些基本环境限制的同时，创造一个具有强烈个性和宁静复杂性的现代场所。

土地上的生活
住宅的每一部分都回应着它所处的独特地段状况。东立面表现为一个凹凸不平的入口，是对"西线"的现代转译。南立面在全部或部分的遮蔽下向大海敞开。西立面将建筑室内与草坪对面的住宅隔开，同时借景可居住海湾对面的水与岩石。北立面则设计成一个可以看到山景的私密庭院。一个布有本土植物和岩石的花园暗示了山与海之间的联系。在住宅中穿行，或是通过住宅的通透，可以完成这种空间上的联系。

在光与空间中穿行
在住宅之中和它周围的运动经过了精心设计，以提高空间的和感官的体验。在平面中形态简单的空间，在高度上则戏剧性地变化，展现了一个预先设计的景色和路线的分层序列。建筑形态和外部空间在互动的对话中对彼此进行了定义。

窗户的布置形成了附近和远处景观的框景，并且展示了光线的运转和流动。面向东北的庭院能捕捉到晨曦，还可抵挡强风。塔状的工作室收集光线，并且有助于空气对流。在4.88米的限高下，它们成为景观中的标志物。整个住宅呈一个房间的进深排列，以使所有的空间都有多面对外，获得了最多的日光和通风。

这幢住宅与环境相和谐，不仅展示了技艺和材料的运用，更营造了一个适于宁静地沉思或是充满活力地社交的避世之所。

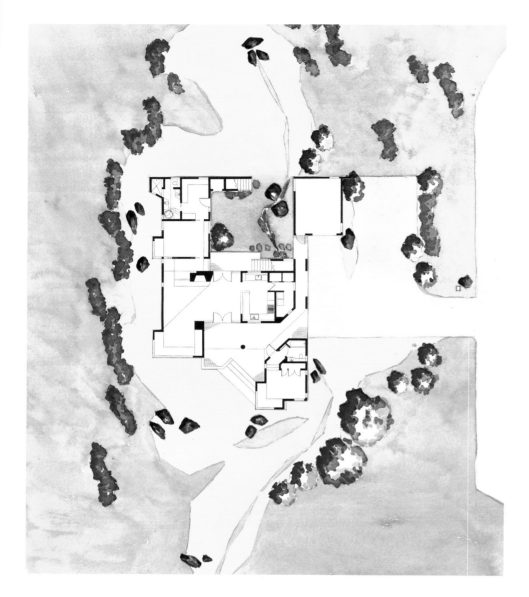

PEG YORKIN HOUSE

PEG YORKIN住宅

This house evolved in response to the tensions of its site, on the edge of a city that sees itself as the edge of the continent. Along the eastern border of the site, the Pacific Coast Highway carries streams of commuters and leisure traffic with their attendant noise, speed and auto induced adrenaline. The Santa Monica Mountains end abruptly east of the PCH. They provide the threat of seasonal fires, a cacophony of new houses since the fire of 1993, and the fragile allure of the indigenous landscape. The western edge of the site is the sandy beach of the Pacific, with stunning and infinitely transforming panoramas. Tightly fit between these two intense habitats is the Yorkin house, designed to provide refuge for three generations of a family sustained by creative and social activism.

MATRIX OF FAMILY LIFE
The house serves as a social and familial retreat for the owner, her two adult children and their families, all of whom were intimately involved in the design process. It was critical for the house to accommodate one person or many with equal comfort, and to support a full spectrum of activities from formal to informal, throughout all seasons. This dense program led to an urban courtyard house typology, a matrix of spaces overlaid with a system of sliding glass and interior panels to provide varying degrees of community and privacy and a range of openness to the environment.

OUTSIDE/INSIDE
The house mediates between dissonant realms, and unfolds as a series of layers that allow for decompression from the intense car culture outside. Entry is through a courtyard of native beach grasses and over a wooden boardwalk. Once inside, the layers progress from more internally focused family areas to open, light-filled social spaces that communicate through sliding glass walls to an exterior courtyard, terrace and beach beyond. Stairs weave vertically through this layering to bring color, light, and openness from above. The roof is developed and expressed as a collection of light scoops and terraces which culminate the vertical spatial movement.

The house expresses the dualities of its site. It is solid and urban on the highway, transparent and transformable toward the water, and permeable and vertically connected to the light and sky.

这所住宅的发展过程应对了地段的局促，这个地段位于一座把自己看作大陆边缘的城市的边缘上。沿着地段东边界的太平海岸高速路上，通勤的乘客与旅游交通伴随着噪音和高速，使人不自觉地心情急躁。在高速路的东边，圣莫尼卡山脉戛然而止。它们的存在带来了季节性火灾的隐患，促成了自1993年大火以来建造的不协调的新房子，并导致了本土景观吸引力的脆弱。而地段的西边则是太平洋具有无穷变化景致的漂亮沙滩。在这两种极端的环境之间，紧密地嵌着为一家三代设计的Yorkin住宅——这是一个具有创造性与社会性的激进主义的家庭。

家庭生活矩阵
这幢住宅是它的主人、主人的两个成年儿女以及他们的各自家庭用于社交和居家的静居之所，他们中的所有人都密切地参与了设计过程。设计的难点在于这幢住宅要在容纳一个人和许多人时保持同样舒适，同时还要适于全年各季节里的各式各样的活动，从正式的到不正式的。这个项目的高密度导致了一个城市庭院型住宅，一个空间矩阵，辅有滑动玻璃和内墙板体系，以提供不同程度的群体性、私密性以及对环境的开放性。

室外/室内
该住宅在不和谐的环境中进行调和，并展开了一系列层次，让人们从外面紧张的车流文化中解压。入口是一个种有本土沙滩草的庭院，下有木板步道。一进入室内，这些层次就从向内聚焦的居家区域向着开放、光线充足的社交区域转化，这些社交区域通过滑动玻璃墙与外部的庭院、平台以及远处的沙滩相通。楼梯在这样的层次中垂直蜿蜒而下，带来色彩、光线和开放性。屋顶被塑造并表达成一系列的采光口和平台，使垂直方向的空间运动达到高潮。

这幢住宅表现了地段的二元性。在高速路的一面它是坚固且城市化的，而面向水的一面则透明、可变，并且垂直地通向日光与天空。

▲
NORTH

5' 10' 20'

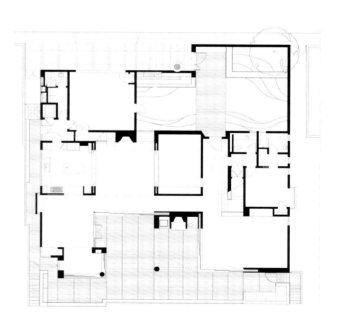

above: ground floor and second floor plan

上图：一层和二层平面图

TANGO, Bo01 HOUSING EXHIBITION

探戈，
Bo01住宅博览会

Bo01, City of Tomorrow, is an ambitious demonstration of sustainable community planning and housing design, which had its public opening in the Spring of 2001. From the re-use of its industrial waterfront site—a classic "brownfield"—to its ultimate goal of complete self-sufficiency, the approximately 1400 units of housing will not depend on Malmö's power or utility grid—Bo01 sets out to be a model of 21st century development. And unlike many of Sweden's annual housing exhibitions, Bo01 is also a permanent settlement, built by public/private investment.

While it is contemporary in execution and spirit, the master plan by Swedish architect Klaus Tam is a delicately-scaled, pedestrian-only village, with a strong perimeter definition—a kind of modern walled town. With the sea on two sides, and a new canal lining the other two, Bo01 is also an island, which heightens the sense of the site as man-made artificial land. The only Americans in the exhibition, we were invited by our Potatisåkern clients to join Bertil Öhrström of FFNS Malmö to design a small, 27-unit block along the canal.

MEDIATING THE ELEMENTS
The Bo01 site feels exposed—the coast at Öresund is often cold, wet, and windy—and the town's walled perimeter has important psychological if not physical advantages for habitation. One side of Tango forms part of this four-story town wall.

WALL AND PAVILION
The town plan's quality of protected enclosure—a tough outside with a soft interior—was compelling enough that we were moved to shape Tango along similar lines: a wall building tautly wraps three sides of a south-fac-ing court. The external construction is rusticated and durable—ribbed pre-cast concrete panels alternate with narrow floor-to-ceiling windows to make a lively but unified façade. From the protection of the walls, glassy bays project out for views and light. Within the court-yard, a set of glass pavilions, like small towers, are gathered around a garden.

FREEDOM AND CHOICE
Given Tango's direct, self-evident concept—wall wraps court—we wanted to set things in motion. The glass towers of different heights declare their independence from the wall by turning slightly as they step around the court—a dance-like movement that inspired our Swedish colleagues to give the project its name. Inside, every apartment has a piece of the wall and part of a glass tower—the tower rooms for living, and the wall spaces divided into bedrooms and baths. Each plan is unique, a special combination and shaping of repeated components, which offers the inhabitants highly individual choices.

I.T. FOR MODERN LIVING
One interesting feature common to all the plans is another wall—an Intelligent Wall. Framed of demountable cabinetry, it runs through the middle of the plan and provides each unit with the cabling and services of a custom-designed information system. While offering programs to enhance future life-styles—integrated vacation planning and away-from-home care, for example—Tango's custom network also monitors the details of power and energy use throughout the day—a treasury of information to help residents and the management streamline their energy profile—an eminently sustainable idea.

Bo01，这个于2001年春天向公众开放的"明日城市"，野心勃勃地展示了可持续的社区规划和住宅设计。从它对水边工业地段——标准"棕地"的重新利用，并达到它的最终目标——实现自给自足，这个大约1400个单元的住宅将不必依赖马尔默的能量和设施供给网络，Bo01开始成为21世纪发展的一个模范。而且不像瑞典的许多其他住宅年展那样，Bo01同时也是个由公众或私人投资修建的永久居所。

虽然它在实际实施和内在精神上都是现代的，但瑞典建筑师Klaus Tam所做的总体规划是一个尺度微妙且仅供步行的村落，并且有一个强烈的边界定义——可以说是一个现代的壁垒城市。它两条边邻海，另两条边由一条新运河形成边界，这又使它成为一个岛，强调了这个地段的人工性质。我们作为参加博览会的唯一美国单位，受到我们的Potatisåkern客户邀请，加入到马尔默的FFNS公司的Bertil Öhrström项目组，沿运河设计一个由27个单元组成的小街区。

协调各种元素
Bo01的地段感觉上是暴露在自然中的——Öresund的海岸通常寒冷、潮湿且有风，于是它的墙壁边界在心理上——如果不是生理上——就成为重要的有利条件。"探戈"的一面就形成了这个4层高的城镇墙壁的一部分。

墙壁与亭阁
城镇规划中体现了一个被保护的闭合场地的性质——一个坚硬的外表和一个柔软的内在，这个有力的性质也打动了我们，让"探戈"遵循了相似的原则：墙面简洁地形成三面，围合着一个南向庭院。建筑的外表面粗糙坚硬，具有耐久性——预制混凝土板和狭长的通高玻璃窗交替排列，形成一个活泼而统一的立面。在三面墙的保护下，几个湾形玻璃体向外伸出以获得良好的景致和光线。在庭院中，一系列的玻璃亭子像小塔一样聚集在一个花园周围。

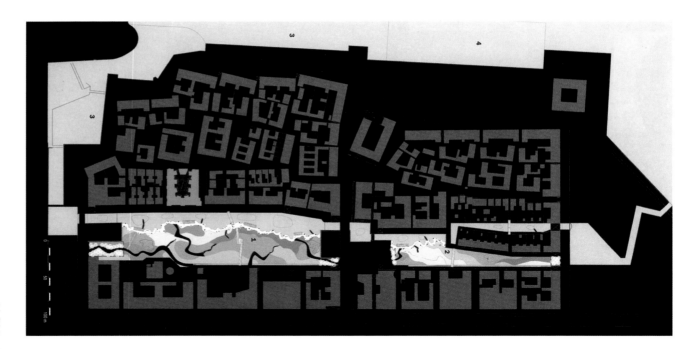

自由和选择权

确定了"探戈"直接、明显的概念——墙壁包围庭院之后，我们想把事物排布在运动系统中。这些不同高度的玻璃塔为了表明它们相对于外墙的独立性，在庭院中进行了轻微地扭转，这种舞步似的动作让我们的瑞典同事给这个项目取了名字。在内部，每个单元都拥有一部分墙壁和一部分玻璃塔——塔中的部分作为起居空间，而墙壁处的空间则成为卧室和卫生间。每个单元的平面都是独一无二的，是对重复元素的独特混合与整形，这给居住者提供了高度个性化的选择权。

现代生活所需的信息技术

有趣的是对所有平面来说还有另一面墙——一面"智能墙"。墙上置有可装卸的细木家具，位于单元平面正中，为每个单元提供了卷缆柱以及定制信息系统的服务。"探戈"不仅提供了提高未来生活方式的服务——比如综合度假规划和离家看管服务，其定制的网络还监控着全天的电力、能量使用细节，为住户和管理人员提供一个信息库，以方便他们整理能量档案——这是一个杰出的可持续概念。

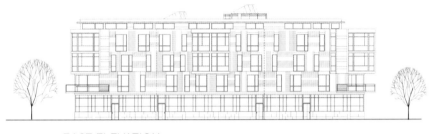

EAST ELEVATION

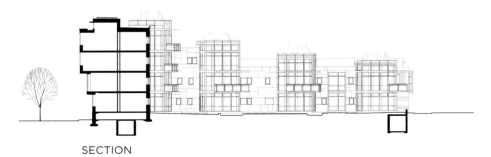

SECTION

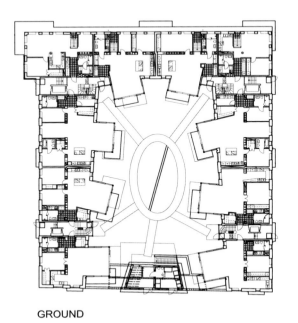

GROUND

TYPICAL

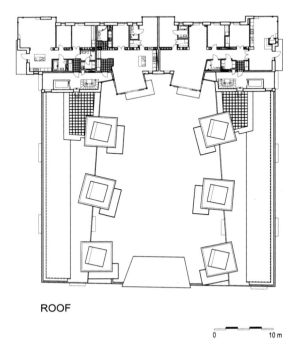

ROOF

0   10 m

Top right: Tango is sited among other iconic buildings such as Ca-latrava's Turning Torso

右上："探戈"沿着Calatrava的螺旋型标志建筑物建立

top left: concept sketch; bottom left: plan showing the "intelligent wall" that connects all units

左上：建筑概念草图
左下：连接所有单元的"智能墙"平面

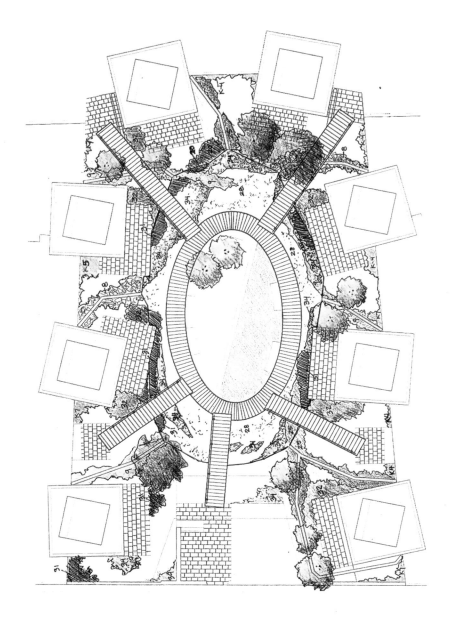

COLOR GARDEN

At the center of the Tango community is a courtyard garden, framed and energized by a Mondrianesque color scheme. The garden itself restates BoO1's ethos as island amid the marshlands: a small elliptical terrace set into a wet garden of mosses and tall grasses, linked to the building by a set of wooden bridges. Private balconies overlook the court, just a few meters from each other: the assumption is, and so far it seems to be working, that anyone unusual enough to live in Tango is going to have some very interesting neighbors!

彩色花园

"探戈"社团的中央是一个庭院花园,一个蒙德里安式的色彩方案包围并激活了它。这个花园本身重现了BoO1的"沼泽地中的孤岛"的概念:在覆满苔藓和高大草本植物的潮湿花园里,伸出一个通过几座木桥与建筑相连的椭圆形小平台。私家的阳台俯瞰着庭院,且彼此相距不过数米,这个设计的初衷是(而且目前看来是成功的):任何一个足够与众不同才能住进"探戈"的人,都将拥有一些非常有趣的邻居!

AMBER BAY RESORT

琥珀湾度假区

CONNECTING THE MOUNTAINS TO THE SEA

This residential resort is located on a spectacular site on the Liaodong Peninsula, outside the city of Dalian, an important port in northeast China. The serene site is backed by the Qianshan Mountain range, and bordered by the Bohai Sea to the west and the Yellow Sea to the east, with an expansive beach toward the southwest, and a picturesque ravine leading to a more secluded beach to the northeast. The siting protectively embraces the project in the tradition of Feng Shui. The project will include ten villas; 58,000 square meters of townhouse and condominium units; clubhouse/recreational amenities; and retail components.

WEAVING OPEN SPACE THROUGH THE SITE

Our goal is to create a new paradigm for coastal residential development in China by focusing on respect for the land and harmony with nature. The design strives to maximize the sense of openness and reduce the apparent density of the buildings. An integrated architectural and open space character is established by closely relating the buildings to the existing geography.

The master plan features a diversity of building types to support the site's topography: a hill-top cluster of villas in the southeast with the most prominent views, town houses arrayed in a splayed configuration overlooking the beach to the southwest, and condominiums defining the north edge and northeast corner of the site.

The project is unified by corridors or "fingers" of open space that weave across the site. These "topographic pathways" provide places for social gathering while optimizing breezes and views for residents. There are three main gestures. One pedestrian path with stepping terraces and stairs meanders from the beach to the ravine through the heart of the site. Another path, slightly more to the south and passing by the villas, has a more natural, informal character. Finally, a curved series of waterfalls along the perimeter Binhai Road fronts the most visible edge of the project and embraces the beach beyond.

THE "MAHJONG" ARCHITECTURAL CONCEPT

Our concept reflects the Chinese culture and its attachment to the traditional tile game of mahjong, which is simple yet complex in its configuration. This is expressed in the architectural massing, which combines rational volumes with picturesque compositions that respond to the site's dramatic conditions. The residential buildings share a language of great rooms punctuated with bays, creating a variety of unit plans while maintaining the continuity of character and expression.

BUILDING VOCABULARY

All of the buildings use a series of elements including protruded bays, trellises, canopies, roof terraces, and gardens to establish a range of scales and connections with the landscape. Simple materials such as bay windows, stone walls and bases are embellished with layers of glassy bands, projections, and loggias to bring maximum daylight into the units and form a memorable roofscape. Green sod roofs have been used as much as possible.

连接山与海

这个居住性的度假区，位于辽东半岛上中国东北的重要港口城市大连市外的一个引人入胜的地段上。这个宁静的地段背靠千山山脉，西面渤海，东临黄海，西南方向有一段广阔的海滩，东北方向则有一条风景如画的山谷通向一段较为偏僻的海滩。从风水的角度来看，地段被环境包围并保护起来。这个项目包含10幢别墅，5.8万平方米的城市联排和公寓单元（condominium），会所和休闲设施以及零售商店。

穿越地形的织入式开放空间

我们的目标是，通过对土地的尊重和与自然达成的和谐，为中国的海滨居住开发项目创造一个新的样本。我们的设计致力于使开放感最大化，并削弱建筑看上去的体量与密度。我们把建筑与原有地形联系起来，建立起一个建筑与开放空间综合的特性。

总体规划中以多种建筑形式为特色，回应了地段的地形：山顶的东南有一群景色最好的别墅；在西南方向的海滩上方排列着联排住宅；而公寓单元则占据了地段的北边界和东北角。

"指形"的开放空间织入地段，形成连廊，将整个项目统一起来。这些"地形通道"为社交集会提供场所，同时也为居民带来了微风和景致。主要有三处设计：一条由台地与台阶组成的步行道从地段中央蜿蜒穿过，从海滩通到峡谷；第二条道路在稍南处，从别墅边经过，性质更为自由、随意；最后，一系列呈曲线排列的瀑布被布置在地段的边界滨海路旁，它们正对着我们的方案，同时环绕着后面的海滩。

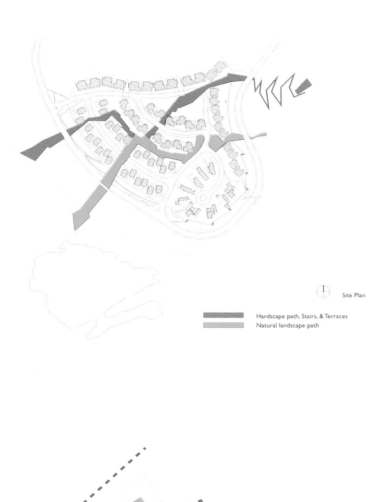

Site Plan

████ Hardscape path, Stairs, & Terraces
████ Natural landscape path

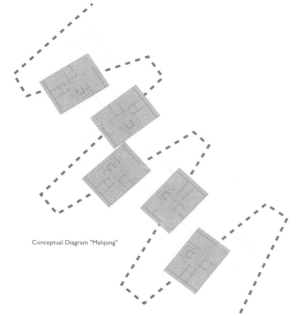

Conceptual Diagram "Mahjong"

SUB FLOOR PLAN   GROUND FLOOR PLAN   SECOND FLOOR PLAN   THIRD FLOOR PLAN

"麻将"建筑概念

我们的建筑概念反映了中国文化以及它对麻将的偏爱，这是一种配置既简单又复杂的游戏。这一点体现在建筑的排布上：理性的体块与风景画般的组合体联合在一起，回应了地段戏剧性的环境。住宅楼采用了被小空间打断的大体块的建筑语言，形成多种单元平面，同时又保持了个性特征和表达方式的连贯性。

建筑语言

所有的建筑运用一系列元素，包括凸室、格架、顶篷、屋顶平台以及花园等，建立了不同的尺度和与景观之间的联系。简单的材料，比如凸窗、石头墙面和基座，装饰以玻璃带、突出物和凉廊等，为单元带来充足的日光并形成一个难忘的屋顶景观。绿色种植屋面得到了尽可能多的使用。

MANZANITA VILLAGE

MANZANITA村

Blessed with an extraordinary site, the architecture of this residential village is shaped to enhance and express community at multiple scales. In response to a site where the campus meets the ocean, we inflected the typologies of the courtyard and the urban square to establish strong social places and connect to the power of the landscape.

Major axes of movement through the project link to the adjacent housing and campus patterns beyond. Active pedestrian paths intersect at a central plaza where housing, dining, and academic uses all have a strong presence and identity. The north-south paseo visually links to the mountains and the ocean. The east-west paseo strategically links a public entry off Ocean Road through the village and to the lagoon.

ANCHORING AND INFLECTING
The village connects to its environment in multiple ways. The exterior paths and courtyards are shaped both to contain community and to orient toward the landscape. Building massing is highest at the central plaza and steps down toward the bluff and lagoon. In plan, the buildings are organized on the campus grid. They are anchored at the central plaza, but inflect as they move out into the landscape to create a more varied set of experiences and views. This duality of being anchored yet moving into the landscape reminds us of natural phenomena, such as kelp or seaweed, whose movement in the water is more varied toward the periphery.

BALANCING THE INDIVIDUAL AND THE COMMUNITY
The buildings are conceived as a three-dimensional "social-plaid," encouraging students and faculty to interact. Social magnets and amenities, such as lounges, studies, kitchens, and laundries, are collected into hubs of activity.

Students can realize their identity at a range of scales. They occupy single or double rooms. Between forty and sixty students occupy a typical "house" with full amenities. Six houses compose each of three quads, accommodating about 270 students each. All eight hundred students share dining, recreational and academic facilities with the existing San Rafael housing to the north.

We were interested in shaping buildings as simple, clear volumes whose details and color occur in socially and environmentally meaningful ways. Entryways, social hubs, bays and porches are richly articulated. Individual room windows are celebrated with colored awnings according to solar orientation.

Tina Beebe's color palette is developed in close response to the landscape. The western quad is based on the palette of the nearby eucalyptus hedgerow. The southeast quad recalls the colors of sand, driftwood, and the beach beyond. The northern quad is inspired by the colors of the lagoon to which it is oriented. The communal dining and academic buildings are more intensely colored, symbolic of the vibrancy of the activity within, yet related to the palettes of the housing. The large white building planes unify the whole village. The color restates the social goals of lively diversification within a harmonious whole.

这个居住性村庄的目的是为了在多重尺度上提高并表达社区的概念。校园与海在这里相接，作为对此的回应，我们改变了庭院和城市广场的类型，创造了很强的社会性空间，并与景观力量建立联系。

这个项目中的主要运动轴线是与旁边的住宅和后面的校园相联系的。具有活力的人行道在一个中心广场处相交，这里汇集着各自有着强烈特性的住宅、餐饮和教学场所。南北方向的散步道在视觉上与山和海形成联系。而东西向的漫步道则有策略地与海滨路上一个穿过村庄通向泻湖的入口相连。

锚固与弯曲
村庄与环境的联系是多方面的。外部的道路和庭院不仅容纳了社区，同时还指向了地形景观。建筑密度在中央广场处最高，向着悬崖和泻湖方向则逐渐降低。从平面上看，这些建筑是按校园的方格网排布的。它们在中央广场处是锚固住的，但在向地景延伸的时候开始弯曲，形成了多样的体验和景象。这种被锚固住同时又向地景移动的二元性让我们想起自然现象，比如海藻和海草，它们在水中的运动也是在外围处更加多样的。

个体与社团间的平衡
这些建筑被设想成三维的"社会方格"，鼓励学生和教员纵向、横向的互动。社交场所和福利设施，比如休闲室、书房、厨房、洗衣房等，都集中在活动中心区里。

学生们可以在不同的尺度上体会到它们的特性。他们住入单人间或双人间；40-60个学生住入一幢设施齐全的"房子"；而6幢这样的房子（能容纳约270名学生）则围合成一个方庭；共有3个这样的方庭。全部800名学生与北边原有的San Rafael住宅共用餐饮、娱乐和教学设施。

Katie Spitz's landscape plan incorporates a spectrum of materials: from urban at the central plaza to restored native grasses at the periphery. Sustainability is enhanced through the use of drought-tolerant planting, bio-swales, permeable paving, and recycled water.

Connecting to the campus, respecting the extraordinary natural site, and supporting a range of social experience has informed our effort to establish a supportive framework for the expression of the individual and the growth of the community.

我们希望建造体量简单清晰，同时细节和色彩具有社会和环境意义的建筑。入口通道、社交中心、隔间以及门廊都经过精心设计。单体房间的窗户则以随太阳方向转动的彩色遮阳棚而闻名。

Tina Beebe的配色方案是与景观密切相关的。西边组团的配色以附近桉树篱的色彩为基础。东南的组团令人想起沙子、木头以及远处海滩的颜色。北边的组团是由它所面向的泻湖的颜色带来灵感。公共餐饮和教学楼的颜色则更为强烈，象征着其中活跃的各种活动，同时又和住宅的颜色相关。大面积的白色平面统一了整座村庄。配色方案再次重申了我们的社会目标：在和谐的整体下呈现活泼的多样变化。

Katie Spitz的景观规划融合了多种材料：从中央广场处的城市材料到在外围的复原的本土草木。通过使用耐干旱植物、生态沼泽、渗水性铺装以及循环用水，提高了环境的可持续性。

与校园的联系、对非凡的自然地段的尊重，以及对各种社交活动的支持，使我们努力建立起一个鼓励个性化表达和社区成长的框架。

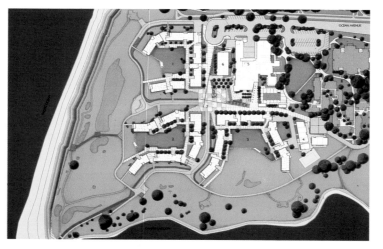

POTATISÅKERN HOUSING

POTATISÅKERN住宅

POTATISÅKERN HOUSING, MALMÖ, SWEDEN

Malmö—at least the central, historic part—and its neighboring university town, Lund, have the visual richness, scale, and tireless appeal of places built by accumulation: narrow streets open unexpectedly onto cobblestone squares and green parks. Small civic buildings, market halls, and train stations focus community activity and add their special character as building types. The town fabric of predominately two-to four-story buildings is made of brick, with tile or metal roofs, and together with the occasional white or colored plaster wall, and the constantly shifting surfaces and details, the whole adds up to a stirring visual treat. In Malmö the scale is more urban, with the added dimension of a variety of waterfronts and edges—a Baltic town that is under-appreciated only because it is outdone by Copenhagen across the water.

The site of Potatisåkern, the eponymous potato field, looks across a waterfront park toward Golden Sound and Copenhagen, and is surrounded by a gentle green district that includes some of Malmö's finest old villas. It is prime real estate—so prime that after years of planning attempts by public and private agencies, no development was quite good enough. In the mid-1980's a consortium of the city's four largest developers decided to seek outside help to break the stalemate.

THE LUXURY OF CHOICE

From our point of view we could say with only slight exaggeration that the project began in 1986 with a ten-minute phone call, was conceived in about forty minutes, and built in sixteen years. During that time the program evolved from its original goal of giving new life and form to classic Swedish social housing, and became market rate rental housing with a luxury standard. For MKB, Malmö's public housing company, the project became a vehicle for a new vision of housing driven not by standardization, but by quality and choice.

AXIS AND CRESCENT

The shaping of Potatisåkern begins with a form for its waterfront edge- a Bath-inspired crescent with a central gap to open the water view to the deep rectangle of the site. From the crescent an axis is drawn through to a neighborhood landmark, the German Church at the back of the site. This central axis is crossed by other visual axes drawn from surrounding streets.

VILLA AND SNAKE

Two complementary building forms, long curvilinear wall-buildings and singular houses or villas, are organized to shape landscape places along the axis and crescent. The gentle meander of the wall-buildings- the "crescent" and the "snake"—mediates their scale as they wind in and out of view. The villas form chorus lines that splay to either side of a grand central lawn, their repeated forms and varied colors and details suggesting an orderly community. These same building types were a feature of our housing at Berlin's Tegel Harbor, but at Potatisåkern their scale was increased considerably, and the whole succeeds largely because the color, detail, and character are very strong.

马尔默——至少它中央的老城部分——以及它附近的大学城Lund，拥有长年积累所形成的丰富的视觉效果、适宜的尺度以及无穷的吸引力：狭窄的街道会不期然地向鹅卵石广场和绿色公园散开。小型的民宅、市场以及火车站聚集了社区活动，并增加了各自的特色。城中主流的2～4层建筑通常是砖砌的，有着瓦片或金属的屋顶，此外偶尔也有白色或彩色的抹灰墙面，还有不断变化的表面和细部，这些共同形成了一个激动人心的视觉盛宴。马尔默的尺度更加城市化，并且有着多样的滨水地带和各式边界——这个波罗的海城市没有得到充分赞誉的唯一理由就是它比水对面的哥本哈根稍为逊色。

我们的地段Potatisåkern是片土豆田地，透过一个滨水公园可以看到Golden Sound和哥本哈根，在它周围则是一片温和的绿色区域，其中包括马尔默最好的一些老别墅。它们是绝好的地产——过于好以致经过几年来公共和私人事务所在规划方面努力，始终都没有形成足够好的开发。20世纪80年代中期，城市中4个最大开发者的联盟决定寻求外部协助以打破这个僵局。

奢侈的选择权

从我们的角度来说，几乎可以不夸张地说，这个工程源于1986年的一个10分钟的电话，用了40分钟构想，却用了16年来建造。在这段时间里，这个项目从其最初的目标——为老式瑞典社会住宅带来新的生命与活力开始，演化成为一个具有奢侈标准的市价出租住宅。对马尔默公共住宅公司(MKB)来说，这个项目将住宅提升到一个新的境界，即不是由标准化驱使，而是由质量和选择权来驱使。

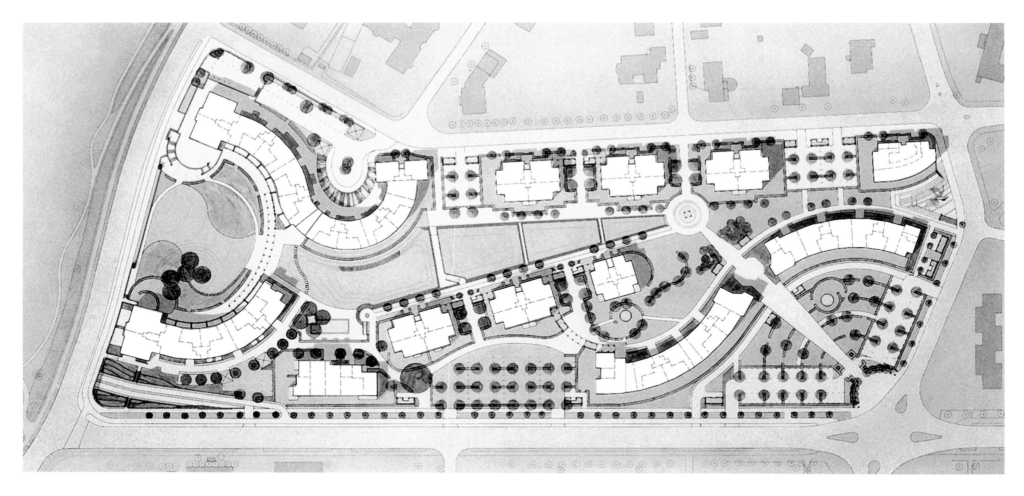

INHABITING THE ROOFTOPS

The making and materials draw directly from the rich context of Malmö and Lund with special attention to the edges of ground and sky. The brick walls of the crescent and snake are completed by zinc paneling at the upper floors and roof, where the architecture merges with the changing atmosphere. In some places, long roof terraces have glassy canopies, and lantern—rooms rise up for distant views. The villas are even more playful: their large roofs come in a variety of materials and colors, sporting chimneys, urns, clerestory windows and dormers to warm up the gray winter skies with an active silhouette. The ochre brick walls of the snake and crescent set a textured background for the brilliantly colored plaster shapes of the villas.

GARDEN GEOMETRIES

Building and landscape are intertwined, and a varied repertoire of garden forms emerges from the strong shaping of the plan. The Crescent Terrace raises a shaggy meadow toward the sea; the adjacent Sun-dial Court, almost always in shadow, is granite-paved with huge roman numerals lit sequentially by low spotlights. The trapezoid of the central Lawn is attended by a series of square gardens and play areas between the villas, and climbs gently to a raised, circular disc—a compass of polished stone, from which axial walks radiate. At the far end of the axis, the last villa and the snake converge and then open out to frame Sailor's Gate, a trumpet-shaped entry place opposite the German Church. In this little square, a play structure of stone and bronze hints at a Viking boat—a detail inspired by the model ships that hang in the foyers of churches all over southern Sweden.

轴线与"新月形"

Potatisåkern的成型是从它滨水处的形式开始的——一个突发灵感产生的新月形，中间有个缺口，将水景引入纵深的长方形地段中。一条轴线从这个新月形开始，延伸到附近的一个地标，地段后面的德国教堂（German Church）。从周围街道引入的其他视觉轴线与这条主要轴线相交。

别墅和"蛇形"

两种基本的建筑形式是：长的曲线形墙式建筑和独幢住宅或别墅，它们的排布形成了轴线上和"新月形"中的景观空间。墙式建筑柔和地蜿蜒，形成"新月形"和"蛇形"，在迂回蜿蜒于视野内外的同时协调着它们的尺度。几幢别墅在中央大草坪的两侧形成附和的列队，它们重复的形式和多样的颜色、细部暗示了一个有秩序的社区。这些建筑类型同样出现在我们在柏林的Tegel港项目中，但在Potatisåkern，它们的尺度大大地增加了，最终因其强烈的色彩、细节和个性而取得了成功。

占领屋顶

建造和取材直接从马尔默和Lund的丰富文脉中吸取灵感，尤其注意了地面和天空两个边界。"新月形"和"蛇形"的砖墙在上面几层和屋顶处改为锌嵌板，以使建筑融入不断变化的大气。在某些地方，长的屋顶平台上长出了玻璃罩和可登高望远的"灯笼"空间。别墅甚至更有趣：它们的大屋顶呈现出多种材料和色彩，竞相展示着烟囱、凹陷、天窗以及老虎窗，形成一道活泼的剪影，点亮了冬天的灰暗天空。"蛇形"和"新月形"的赭石砖墙为涂有彩色抹灰的别墅形成了一个有肌理的背景。

花园的几何布置

建筑与景观交融在一起，在平面的强烈形态中体现了异彩纷呈的花园形式。新月形平台上，一片疏松的草坪面向大海；与之相邻的日晷庭院由花岗岩铺就，由于长年处于阴影中，在其中布置由持续的微弱聚光灯照亮的巨大罗马数字。中央的梯形草坪由一系列方形花园和别墅间的玩耍区域组成，逐渐爬升到一个抬高的圆盘——一个抛光石广场上，从这里发射出轴线式步道。在轴线的远端，最后一幢别墅和"蛇形"相互靠拢，然后又相互分离，露出"水手大门"——一个正对德国教堂的喇叭形入口。在这个小广场上，一个由石材和铜制的小品建筑暗示了一艘海盗船，这个细节的灵感来自于瑞典南部所有教堂的大厅中悬挂的船只模型。

TIANJIN XIN-HE
MASTER PLAN
+ HOUSING

天津新河区住宅城总体规划

The Tanggu Region near the port city of Tianjin is expected to be the major residential area to support the new Teda Area development. Moore Ruble Yudell's master plan aims to complete an attractive residential city that offers a full range of recreational facilities and amenities. The new program on the site and its benefits to the overall Tanggu region will establish a modernized, well-equipped city and a residential center that will eventually replace the Tanggu Old Town as the residential hub of the Tanggu region.

MASTER PLAN CONCEPT
The master plan is informed by the goals of celebrating human activity and interaction, nurturing community, and connecting the residents to their urban context and natural environment. The defining framework will be a harmonious interplay of residential blocks, a sequence of canals, and a meandering waterfront to create lively pedestrian-centered neighborhoods. The artful shaping of spaces, paths of movement, qualities of entry and identity will work together to support creative interaction at multiple scales. A series of canals and waterfront features, while honoring the great traditions of Western and Chinese landscape design, will provide an attractive amenity to accommodate a wide variety of recreational uses. A series of islands accessed by bridges within a man-made lake offer places apart for civic and cultural uses and horticultural parks, as well as more remote residential habitats. A gridded system of walkable streets at human scale will engender a comfortable and habitable place that fosters community. Designed at multiple scales of habitation, open spaces and water features, building massing and heights, and the space between buildings will be carefully balanced to frame vistas, animate public plazas and promenades, and create serene courtyards.

NEIGHBORHOODS
The master plan designates a series of themed neighborhoods, each with its own identity, parks, and open spaces. The character of each neighborhood will be defined by the types of residential buildings (bar building, curved building, or villas), as well as the conditions in and around that neighborhood (meandering waterfront, islands, canals, public spaces). All residential streets are oriented to the waterfront promenade to provide a coherent visual and physical connection to the canals and waterfront. Residential unit types include high-end, mid-range, and low-end units. High-end units consist of villas and townhouse types; mid-range units consist of condominium types; and low-end units consist of apartments. The massing of the buildings steps from lower villas along the lake to taller apartment buildings at the outer periphery of the site. The high-end units are closest to the lake and the low-end apartments are toward the outer periphery of the property, with the mid-range units in between.

港口城市天津下属的塘沽区，将成为支持天津泰达经济技术开发区（TEDA）发展的主要居住区。MRY总体规划的目标是建立一个提供全套娱乐设施和便捷服务的有吸引力的住宅城。这个新项目及它为整个塘沽区带来的利益将形成一个装备齐全的现代化城市和一个居住中心，最终将取代塘沽老城成为塘沽区的居住核心。

总体规划概念
总体规划的目标是：展示人的活动与交流，培养社区，并将居民与城市文脉和自然环境联系起来。纲领性的大框架是：通过居住街区间的和谐互动、运河形成的序列以及一条蜿蜒的滨水边界来创造以行人为中心的活力街坊。巧妙的空间布置、运动路线、入口质量以及独特的个性将在多重尺度上共同形成创造性的互动。一系列的运河及滨水景观，发扬了西方和中国景观设计的伟大传统，将提供能满足多种娱乐用途的诱人便捷设施。在一个人工湖中由桥梁连接的一系列岛屿将包含市政、文化以及园艺公园等用地，同时也提供一些更僻静的居住环境。一个由可步行的人性尺度街道组成的网格系统将形成一个舒适的、可居住的空间，帮助形成社区。在多种尺度上设计的开放空间及滨水景观，建筑的密度和高度以及建筑之间的空间将得到细心的权衡，以形成街景，激活公共广场和散步场所，并营造宁静的庭院。

PEDESTRIAN CIRCULATION: CONTINUOUS MOVEMENT

The circulation network for pedestrians, joggers and bicyclists is organized in a strategy of "continuous movement." Paths are linked and interconnected with each other, resulting in a design without "dead ends" or cul-de-sacs. This continuous movement encourages exploration of the diverse spatial experiences of the residential areas while reinforcing the sense of connection to community. An especially important aspect of the circulation design is the network paths that connect the different places along the waterfront promenade. Neighborhood-scaled kindergarten schools and retail spaces are interspersed within the residential blocks to allow for convenient, walkable access to childcare and local goods and services.

WATER NETWORK

A man-made meandering lake connected by small channels to the main Xinhe Canal winds through the site and is punctuated by several islands for residential and leisure functions. The lake provides a welcome open space for activities along its edges: sports including ice-skating, boating, fishing, and swimming, as well as walking, picnics, and tai-chi. There will also be a range of outdoor performance spaces, a Museum, Library, and a Theater, as well as playgrounds, pavilions, and tea houses.

邻 里

总体规划中分配了一系列的主题街坊，每个街坊都有自己的身份、公园以及开发空间。每个街坊的性质将由居住建筑的形式（长条形、曲线形或是别墅）以及街坊内外部的环境（蜿蜒的滨水线、岛屿、运河、公共空间）决定。所有的居住性街道都朝向滨水步道，与运河和滨水区域建立起连贯的视觉和实质联系。住宅单元的类型包括高端、中级和低端。高端单元由别墅和联排组成；中级单元由私人占有公寓（condominium）组成；低端单元则由公寓楼组成。建筑的密度从湖边的低矮别墅上升到地段外围处较高的公寓楼。高端单元离湖最近，低端公寓则在外围，中级单元则夹在它们中间。

行人流线："连贯运动"

行人、慢跑者和骑自行车的人的流线网络被组织在一个"连贯运动"的方案中。道路互相连接、交叉，不会出现"死胡同"。这种连贯运动提供了住宅区内不同空间的体验，同时加强了与社区的联系感。在这个流线方案中，将滨水步道边的不同空间联系起来的网状道路尤其重要。街坊尺度的幼儿园、学校和零售空间散布在居住街区内，以保证可以方便快捷地到达托幼、购物等各种服务设施。

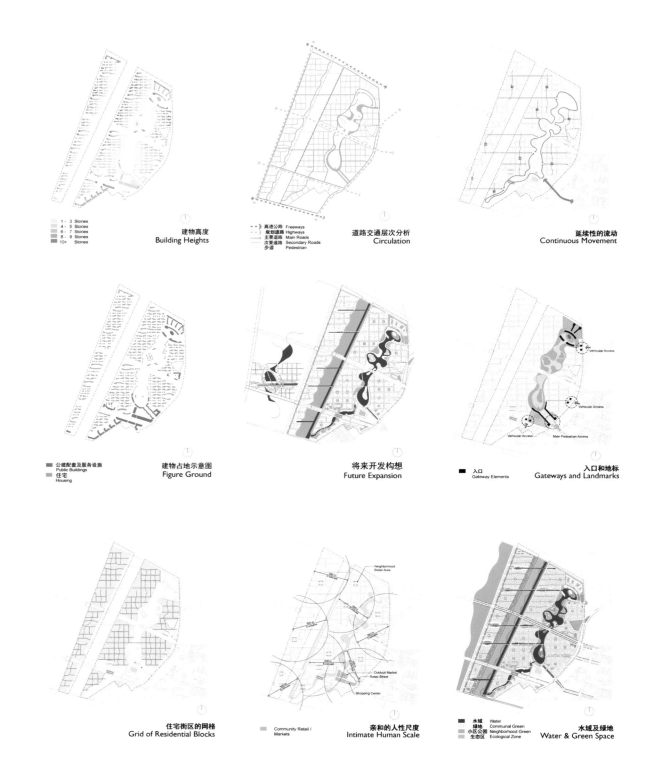

在地段中有一个通过小运河与新河主运河相连的蜿蜒的人工湖泊，其中点缀着几个用于居住和休闲的小岛。湖岸提供了令人愉快的开放空间，可以进行各种活动：体育运动（如滑冰、划船、钓鱼和游泳等），散步，野餐，打太极拳等。还会有一些室外观演场所，一座博物馆，一个图书馆以及一个剧院，另外还有运动场、亭子和茶室。

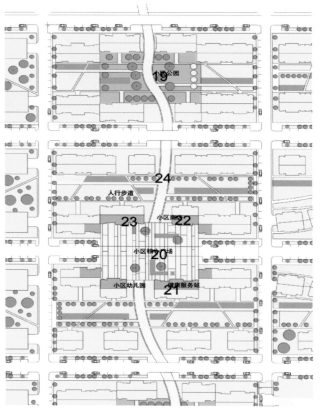

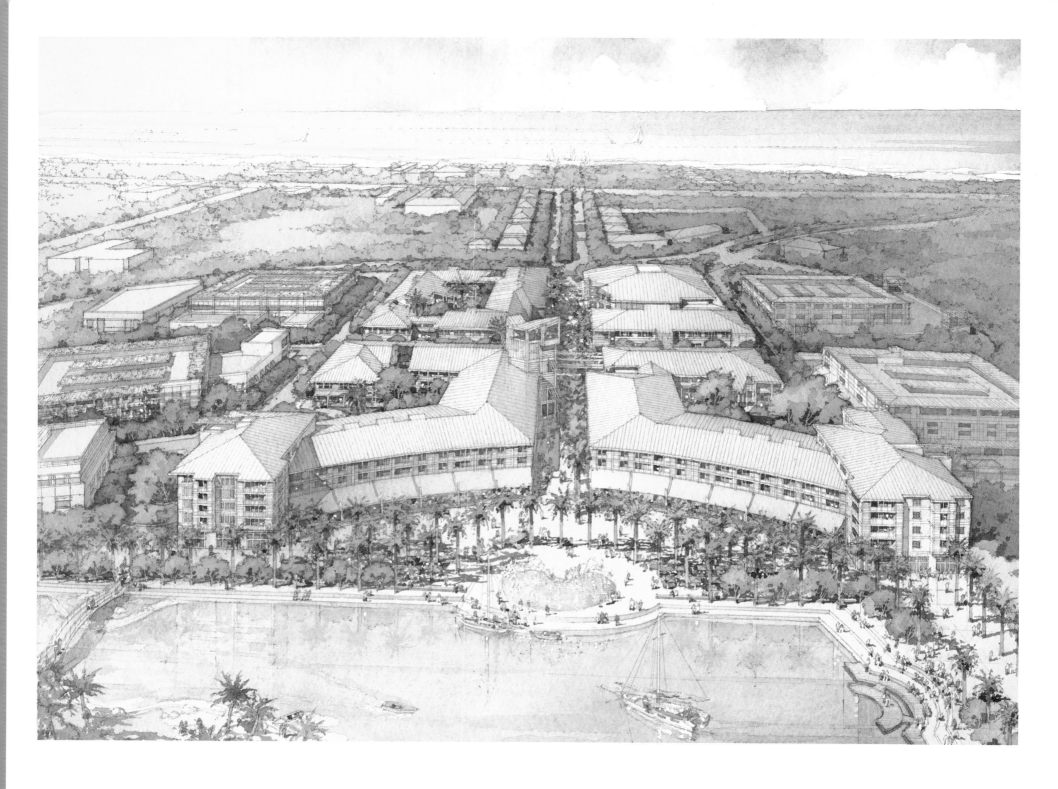

CAMANA BAY

CAMANA 海湾

The new Camana Bay project presents an opportunity to create a community that is uniquely of the place. It is a sustainable community that is responsive to the site, landscape, climate, and culture of the island. Yet it is conceived and is being built with contemporary materials, technologies, and methods. This will be a lively and diverse mixed-use community accommodating residents, visitors, and those who work there. The landscape and architecture has a range of expression within a harmonious whole.

One key challenge in creating new communities is the necessity to avoid a mono-culture. Working with Cayman Shores Development Ltd. (CSDL) and a range of talented design and technical consultants, it was important to develop an approach to the community that would allow for the full range of activities of daily life (living, working, shopping, education, recreation). In addition, the plan envisions a wide array of housing types, from apartments to single family houses to multi-unit housing. These represent a significant range of affordability. The plan is established to encourage pedestrian interaction as well as to encourage the possibility of working and living in the same neighborhood. The architecture and landscape reflect the climate and culture of the island and yet they are not overly nostalgic. They evoke the place while being designed as fresh, contemporary expressions which are sensitive to their context and site.

Another challenge is to create a community that can evolve, adapt, and grow over time. To address this, the design team and CSDL have created a master plan that serves as a powerful armature for a strong sense of place, but is flexible. The careful design of the hierarchy of different kinds of pedestrian paths, lanes, and streets, as well as a diversity of landscape and street planting is a way to create a strong identity even as the uses may change over time. Similarly there is a strong armature of community-serving uses, such as parks, waterfront, cultural, recreational, and educational amenities. These form a vital commitment to a lasting community.

A third challenge is how to create a community that has both diversity of expression and an overall harmony of experience. The design team has developed both master plan and architectural guidelines to allow individual owners or tenants to express the special qualities of their own identity and vision.

新的Camana海湾项目为营造一个独一无二地属于这个场所的社区提供了一个机会。这是一个可持续的社区，对地段、景观、气候以及岛的文化作出了回应。然而，它的构思和建造用的是当代的材料、技术和方法。它将成为一个有活力且多样化的具有混合功能的社区，接待并容纳居民、访客以及在这里工作的人。景观和建筑在一个协调的整体里呈现出不同的表达。

营造新社区所面临的一个关键挑战是要避免单一的文化。我们与Cayman Shores发展有限公司（CSDL）以及一系列有才华的设计和技术顾问合作，认为非常需要创造出一种可以容纳齐全的日常活动（起居、工作、购物、教育、娱乐）的社区。另外，我们的方案构想了多种住宅类型，从公寓楼到家庭独幢房屋再到多单元住宅。它们构成了一个广阔的经济负担范围。方案中鼓励人的互动，并增加了在同一个街区中工作、生活的可能性。建筑和景观反映出该岛的气候与文化，但并不过于怀旧。它们唤醒了场所，同时又呈现出新鲜的当代表达，体现出对文脉和地段的敏感。

另一个挑战是要使营造出的社区可以随着时间演变、适应并生长。于是，设计小组和CSDL一起建立了一个总体规划，它形成了一个具有强烈场所感的有力骨架，同时，它又是灵活可变的，随着时间可以不断生长、适应。为此，我们精心设计了不同等级的多种行人道路、小径和街道，以及多种景观和街道种植，即使它们的功能以后会改变，也将营造出强烈的特性。与之类似，还有一个社区服务设施的有力骨架，包括公园，滨水功能，文化、娱乐和教育设施等。它们有力地保证了这个社区是持久的，可以随着时间适应和改变。

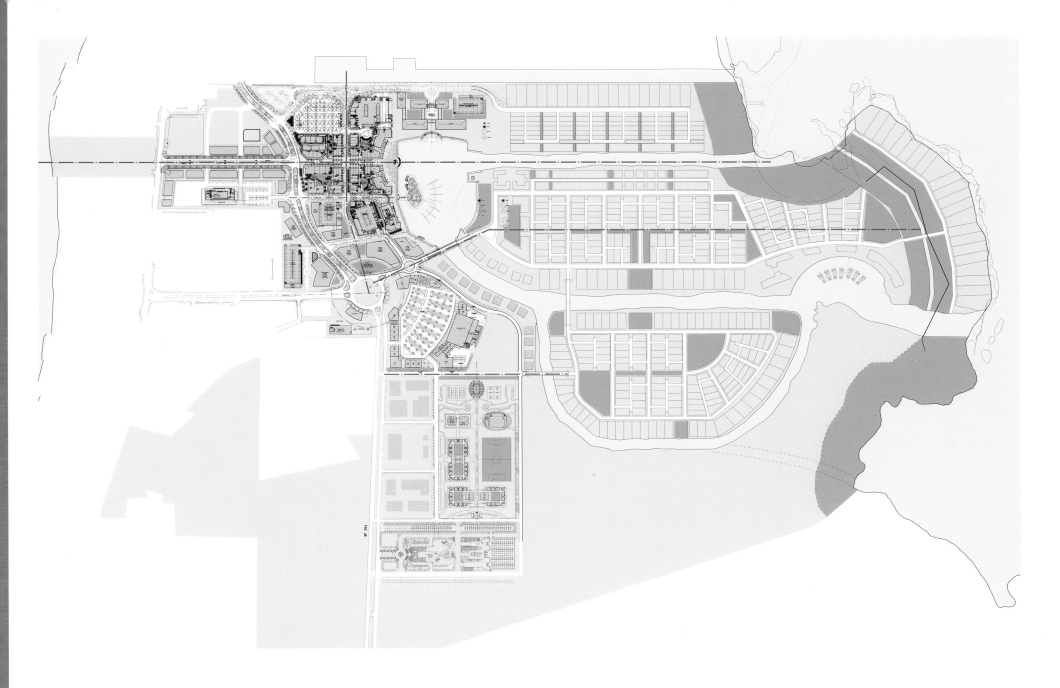

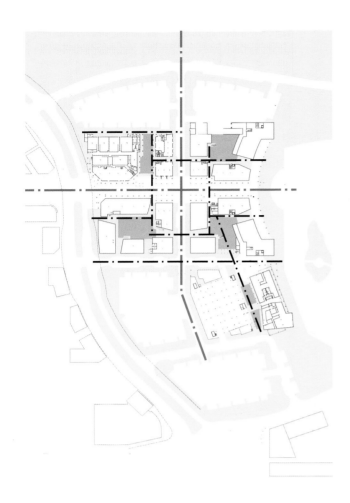

第三个挑战是如何营造一个社区，既有多样化的表达，又有一个整体的协调体验。为此，设计小组既做了总体规划又制定了建筑的指导路线，保证了一定程度的协调，同时也允许个体业主和房客表达他们自己身份、视角的独特性质。

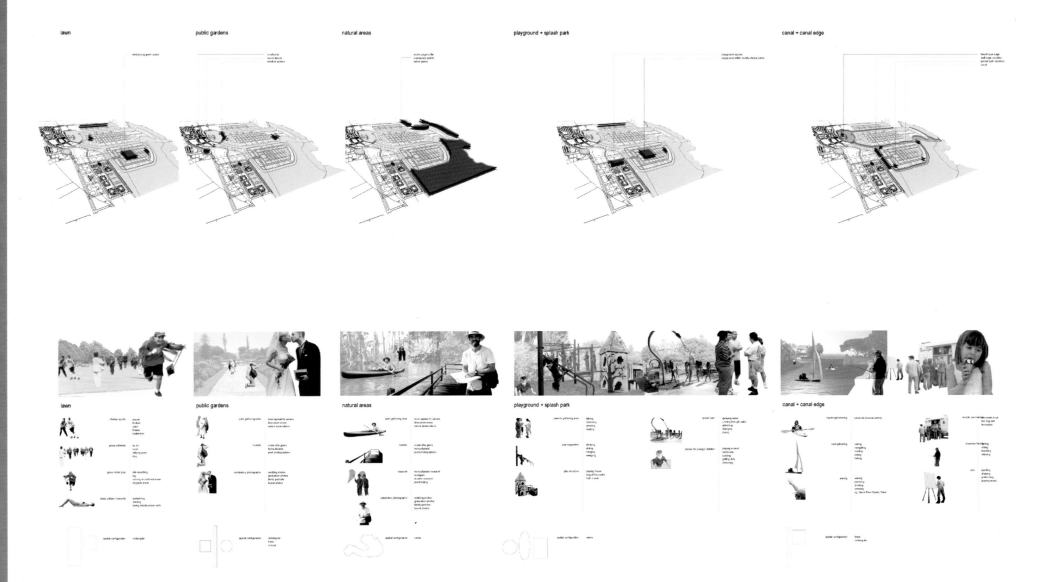

lawn　　　　　public gardens　　　　　natural areas　　　　　playground + splash park　　　　　canal + canal edge

above: studies for open space uses　　　　　上图：开放空间用途研究

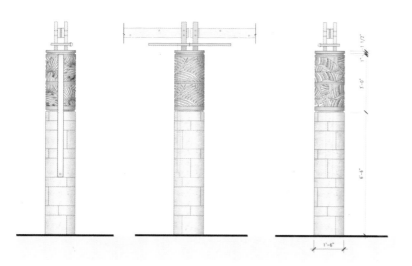

above: original expressions for ornamental details, including light-ing, screens, railings, and columns, reflect the indigenous flora

上图：装饰细部原创表达，包括：采光，屏幕，栏杆，梁柱，对当地建筑风格的反映

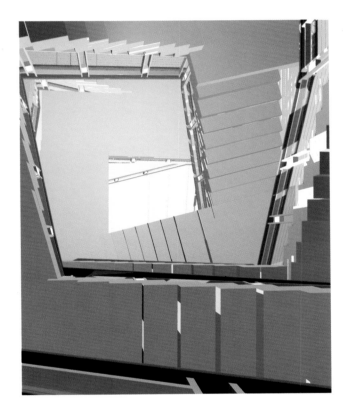

above: architectural elements such as louvers and sun shades are derived from environmental precedents　上图：百叶窗和光影等建筑元素的灵感来源于环境的惯例

02   REACHING OUT

CONNECTING CULTURE AND COMMUNITY

伸展　连接文化与社区

我们的建筑与城市设计的关键性角色是在帮助充实社区，并为人们提供共同体验和文化发展的交流平台。我们对建筑的塑造有助于将人与场所联系起来，继而加强了我们社区的文化活力。这在多重尺度上发生着，包括街道上和走廊里的偶然互动，以及音乐厅或是教室中的有组织的体验。建筑物可以被塑造成为这种能量化的发展的互动矩阵，它对我们的文化革新是非常重要的。

Our buildings and our cities play a central role in helping to nurture community and in providing the vessels for our shared experiences and cultural growth. By shaping buildings to help connect people and places, we can reinforce the cultural vitality of our communities. This happens at many scales and includes the serendipitous interaction on the street or in the corridor as well as the structured experience of the concert hall or classroom. Architecture can be shaped to energize this ongoing matrix of interaction, which is central to our cultural evolution.

UNITED STATES COURTHOUSE

美国联邦法院大楼

The courthouse is a classic building type, deeply associated with American history, place, and culture. Contemporary courthouses have evolved into a new type, with altogether different problems of scale, organization, security, and functional complexity—yet at their core, the original courtroom can still be found, with its sense of decorum and drama. The challenge of modern courthouse design is to find appropriate expression for the building as a representation of the civic institution of the law, and for the Federal Courthouse, as a symbol of the Federal Government in a local place. In terms of place, Fresno's downtown civic district had but few landmarks. The true context of the Courthouse, appropriate to its regional function, is the agricultural landscape surrounding the city—California's great Central Valley.

ICONIC SHAPING
Fresno's new courthouse is large—a result of its program and the two-story height of the typical courthouse floor—and sufficiently imposing by its sheer mass that we sought ways to divide, articulate, open up, and lighten the form into numerous parts. This complexity, which is also inherent in the program, is then re-unified by shaping. The shaping of the courthouse draws on the power of familiar local monuments—the nearby Sierra Nevadas. The mass is folded into an L of two intersecting volumes, with solid shoulders and sloping tops. At the apex, a grand loggia frames views over Fresno's green suburbs, the tree plantations of the Valley, and the snow-capped peaks.

PORCH AND PANORAMA
Embracing landscape qualities as varied as the region's mountain streams, oak dotted foothills, and sweeping agricultural plains, the site design of the courthouse is all about place. The L of the building frames a large public garden, designed as a tableau to be seen from the lobby, a tall glassy porch. Few courthouse lobbies offer this kind of continuous experience of landscape: one enters along a walk tangent to the garden, turns through a vestibule, and crossing the lobby looks back at the outdoor composition, a kind of living diorama. Artists Anna Valentina Murch and Douglas Hollis have heightened the experience by bringing thematic landscape elements—rocks from their stream-bed fountain, a well, and the abstract grid of an orange grove—into the lobby itself.

GALLERIES OF LIGHT AND LITIGATION
From the lobby—garden, courthouse visitors are brought to elevators serving stacks of glassy galleries poised over the courtyard, looking back to the city. As settings for pre-trial activity, the galleries are not insignificant—they are places where deals, strategies, and moments of truth occur that have ultimate importance in the individual and collective lives of the people. The glass walls of the galleries are gently bowed, playing against the solid, textured concrete walls of the building and giving a subtle sense of pressure—the flow of human activity and destiny held within the solid frame of the law.

法院是一种经典的建筑类型，与美国的历史、地理和文化密切相关。现代的法院已经演变为一种新的类型，面临着完全异于以前的尺度、组织、安全以及功能复杂性方面的问题，但是在它们的核心，依旧能找到原始的审判庭，以及原始的礼仪感和戏剧感。现代法院设计所面临的挑战，是要找到合理的表达方式，对这个建筑来说，使它成为城市法律机构的代表；而对联邦法院来说，使它成为联邦政府在地方上的一个象征。从地段来看，弗雷斯诺的中心城区只有少数几个地标。法院所处的合乎于其地区功能的真正文脉是城市周围的农业景观——加利福尼亚的中央大峡谷。

标志性的造型
出于项目的要求并且由于典型的法院层高通常是平常的两倍，弗雷斯诺新法庭将是一座很大的建筑，而且它挺拔的体量十分宏伟，所以我们试图将其分割、清楚地表达、展开，并将其形式柔化为几个部分。于是这个来源于项目的复杂性将通过其造型得到重新统一。法院大楼的造型所吸取的力量来自当地熟悉的地标——附近的内华达山脉。这个体块被折叠成一个L形，由两个相交的体量组成，具有坚硬的棱角和倾斜的屋顶。从最高处的大凉廊，可以看到弗雷斯诺的绿色郊区、峡谷里的树木种植以及积雪覆顶的山峰。

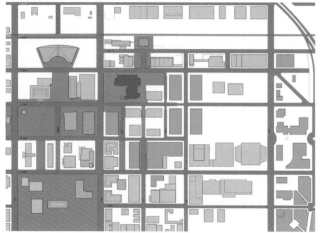

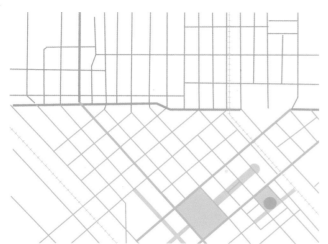

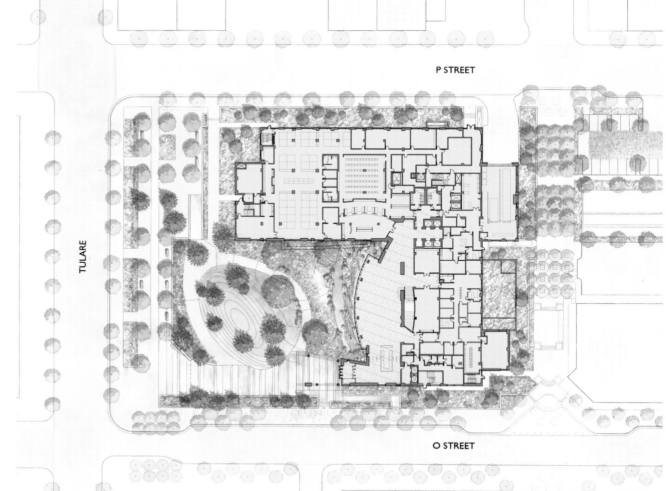

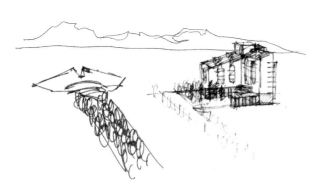

门廊和全景

法院的场地设计借鉴了各式各样的景观性质，比如山间溪流、缀有橡树的丘陵以及开阔的农业草原，完全与地段相关。L形建筑形成了一个大的公共花园，设计成从休息厅——一个高大的玻璃门廊——可以看到的生动场景。很少有法院的休息厅能提供这种连续的景观体验：沿着与花园相切的步道进入，转而穿过一个前厅，然后透过休息厅回望到室外的景致，就像一幅生动的透视画一般。Valentina Murch和Doug Hollis两位艺术家把主题性的景观元素——河床喷泉上的岩石、一口井以及一个抽象的橘林格网引入到大厅内部，更加增强了这种体验。

充满光明的法律展廊

法院的访客可以从休息厅来到电梯间，从这里可以通往一系列玻璃展廊，它们位于庭院上方，回望着城市。作为审判前的活动场所，这些展廊十分重要：它们见证了协议、战略和真理时刻，这些对个体和集体人类来说是最重要的东西。展廊的玻璃墙面微微弯曲，与建筑坚硬、有纹理的混凝土外墙形成对比，并显示出一种微妙的压迫感——存在于法律坚固的框架之中的人类行为和命运的流动。

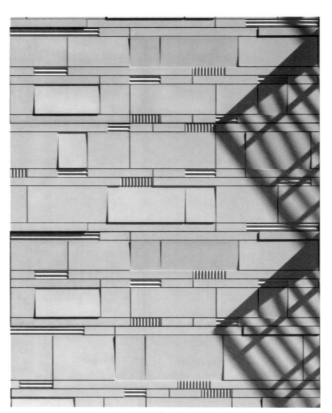

DYNAMIC RUSTICATION

One of the defining aspects of the courthouse is its unique skin of sculptural precast concrete. Although precast concrete is commonly deployed as an exterior cladding material, it has seldom been manipulated to such dramatic effect as it has been for this courthouse.

The variation of concrete surface patterns across the elevations of the courthouse are intended to suggest the rugged nature of the landscape in the region, particularly the majestic faces of the Sierra Nevada Mountains rising to the east. The concrete also makes a sharp contrast with the smooth glass of the curtain wall elements it frames. The artistic effect of the concrete mimics a mesmerizing display found in nature: throughout the day, as the sun travels across the sky, the walls of the building become an ever-changing tapestry of light and shadow.

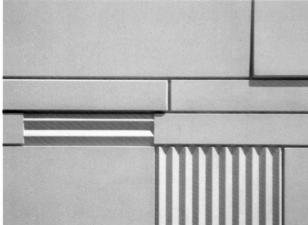

动态的肌理

这个法院最重要的外观特征之一就是它那独特的雕塑般的预制混凝土表皮。尽管预制混凝土被广泛地用于外表面覆盖材质，但它很少被处理得像在这个法院里那么戏剧性。

法院的立面上混凝土表皮的多种模式是为了暗示当地景观的粗犷性质，尤其是在东边伫立的内华达山脉的宏伟外观。混凝土同时还与它所包围的光滑玻璃幕墙形成强烈对比。混凝土的艺术效果模仿了一个自然界现象：一天之中，太阳在空中移动，建筑的墙面就变成了一幅不断变化的光影织锦。

above: Artists Anna Valentina Murch and Douglas Hollis drew inspiration from the region to create landscape and water elements for the courthouse.

上图：艺术家 Anna Valentina Murch和Douglas Hollis受宗教启示为法院所作的景观和水利设计

SANTA MONICA PUBLIC LIBRARY

圣莫尼卡公共图书馆

The Santa Monica Public Library occupies half a city block on the downtown site of the former Main Library. The old library was one of the city's most popular institutions, but it had become outdated and was in need of improvement. The program for the new library is moderate in size, but great in ambition. Our clients wanted no less than a model twenty-first century library: friendly and service-oriented, flexible, with the latest in information systems, a certified LEED® Silver rating for sustainability, abundant below-grade parking, and a café that would allow the facility to become "the living room of the city." The size of the site is generous for the Library program, thus allowing for flexible planning and room to expand.

A CIVIC PRESENCE THAT ACTIVATES THE STREET
Despite the classic library dictum of a single guarded entrance, it was important to connect the library as closely as possible to its surrounding edges. The design allows entrances on all sides that welcome visitors, guiding them to a main entry gallery at the center of the block. The entry gallery is controlled by magnetometers and the central circulation desk.

AN OPEN AND INVITING PLACE FOR COMMUNITY
Reader spaces within the Library are visible from the street, lending a sense of transparency to the public areas of the building. The principal elevation along a major boulevard presents a long, narrow, two-story reading room with continuous floor-to-ceiling windows. At the base of the window, banquette seating under a low canopy creates an intimate edge poised slightly above the sidewalk. Other spaces feature bay windows at upper levels, with views to the mountains and ocean beyond.

A PROTECTED INTERIOR COURTYARD FOR REFLECTION AND COMMUNITY
The larger setting of the Library is a green city, with a famed collection of street trees and numerous parks. In keeping with this quality, Library interiors are interspersed with pocket gardens, which enrich the street edges as well as light the interiors. At the center of the whole is a large enclosed garden court, with controlled access that permits the space to be used by Library readers. A small café with wireless connectivity animates the court and provides a sociable neighborhood destination. Carl Cheng, the project's public artist, has introduced a broad, circular canopy that intersects the glassy corner of the café. Using open steel trellis-work, transparent colored digital image lenses, and adjacency to a reflecting pool, the canopy elicits a dreamy space filled with watery reflections and filtered colored light: an evocation of the undersea world of the nearby bay. With a planting palette of cool colors and picturesque forms, the landscape architect's garden design continues the underwater effect.

A SUSTAINABLE WORKPLACE AND COMMUNITY CENTER
The program works best in a two-story scheme—a challenge in creating the kind of scale that would make a civic focal point within the Library's commercial/residential district. The inverted roof form, a classic Roman-style impluvium, makes the highest part of the building out at the street edge, sloping gently down into the central garden The roof slope is expressed at the interior, giving variety and character to the large open spaces of the second floor Reference Library.

圣莫尼卡公共图书馆位于原来的图书馆地段上，占据了半个城市街区。原来的图书馆曾是城市中最受欢迎的场所，但现在已经过时，需要改进。这个新图书馆项目在尺度上是平凡的，但具有不凡的野心。我们的客户想要的正是一个标准的21世纪图书馆：友好，服务周到，灵活可变，拥有最先进的信息系统，具有可持续性LEED银奖资格证明，足够的地下停车位，还要有一个咖啡厅，使得这个图书馆变成"城市的起居室"。地段的面积很充裕，提供了灵活布局和增加房间的机会。

以市民姿态激活街道
以往的图书馆通常只有一个有人看守的入口，然而将图书馆尽可能密切地与其周围界面联系起来是很重要的。我们的设计在各个方向都有入口，欢迎访客进入，并引导他们到达建筑中央的一个主要入口长廊。这个入口长廊则是由磁强计和中央循环室来控制的。

开放、引人的社区空间
图书馆中的阅览空间是可以从街上看见的，这为建筑的公共空间营造了一种透明的感觉。主干道上的主立面展现了一面长而狭窄的窗户通高的两层阅览室。在窗户底部，一个低矮雨棚下的窗口凳形成了略高于人行道的一条亲切的边缘。上面几层的其他空间则具有可以看到远处山和海的特色凸窗。

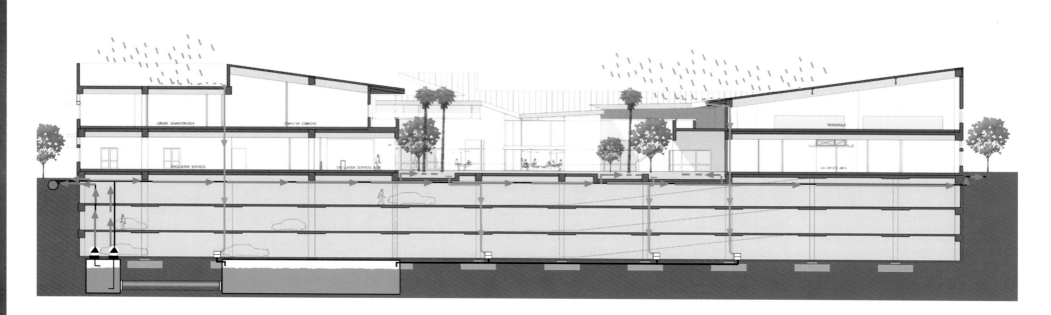

above: integrating sustainability—rain water from the impluvium roof is collected, filtered, and stored in a cistern for landscape irrigation

上图：可持续性整合， impluvium材质屋顶可收集雨水，过滤后储存到水箱以备景观灌溉之需

Sustainable or "green" design features meet high standards. High windows with sun controls bring natural light deeply into the spaces, integrated with the perimeter lighting system. The low heat-absorbing roof collects rain water, which is filtered and stored in a 220,000 gallon underground cistern for use in the landscape. The use of sustainable materials (renewable resources, recycled content, and healthy materials) in public and office areas supports a high level of workplace quality for users and staff. Under-floor plenum air supply in public areas promotes energy efficiency and the use of fresh air for higher indoor air quality.

Project delivery also provided a model for the City—a design-build process that teamed the design firm with a contractor chosen on the basis of qualifications.

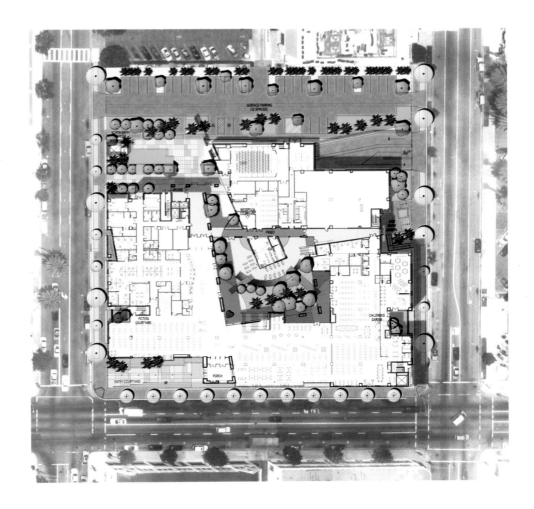

一个适于思考和交际的内部庭院

图书馆所处的大环境是一座绿色城市，有著名的种类齐全的行道树以及几座公园。为了保持这种特质，图书馆内部散布着袖珍花园，不仅丰富了街道界面，同时也为室内增辉。在整体的中央有一个大型的闭合庭园，其受控的入口保证了只有图书馆读者才能使用这个空间。一个无线网络覆盖的小咖啡厅激活了这个庭园，并为邻里提供了一个友善的去处。这个项目的公共艺术家Carl Cheng设计了一个与咖啡厅玻璃转角相交的宽阔圆形顶棚。这个顶棚运用了开放的钢构架和透明的彩色数码图像镜片，并且紧邻一个反光的水池，营造出一个充满了水波倒影和彩色光芒的梦境，唤起人们对附近海湾海底世界的联想。景观设计师在花园中运用冷色调的种植和风景画般的形式，延续了这种水底的效果。

一个可持续的工作场所和社区中心

该项目在两层方案中得到充分发挥，很好地营造出在图书馆所处的商住区内一个城市焦点的尺度。向内倾斜的屋顶形式，以及庭院中的古罗马式方形蓄水池使得建筑在街边达到最高点，并缓缓地坡向中央的公园。屋顶的坡度在内部体现出来，给二层资料馆的大型开放空间增加了多样性和独特的个性。

该项目的可持续性或者说"绿色"设计也达到了很高的标准。由太阳控制的高窗将自然光引入空间底部，与周边的照明系统结合。低矮的吸热屋顶同时收集雨水，雨水经过过滤，作为景观用水储存在地下1,000,140升的蓄水池中。在公共和办公区域所运用的可持续材料（可更新的资源、再生材料以及对健康有益的材料）保证了读者阅读和员工工作环境的高质量。公共区域地板下的强制通风提高了能源效率并促进了新鲜空气的使用，使室内达到更高的空气标准。

这个工程各阶段间的移交、承接也为该市提供了样板：设计建造的过程使设计事务所与按资格选定的承包商共同形成团队。

SANTA MONICA CIVIC PARKING STRUCTURE

SANTA MONICA, CALIFORNIA, USA
圣莫尼卡，加利福尼亚州，美国

圣莫尼卡市内停车场

A CIVIC GATEWAY

A recently completed master plan for the Civic Center designates a new civic gateway at Fourth Street and the new Olympic Drive to the new district that includes the renovated historic City Hall and Courthouse, and the new Public Safety Building. Intended as an integral part that completes a quadrant of civic buildings, the new structure will provide 900 parking spaces on six levels above grade and two below grade while visually uniting the tableau of diverse buildings. The design team was additionally challenged to create a building that exemplified the city's commitment to sustainable design while strengthening the urban fabric and providing public amenities.

One of the challenges for this project is to create architecture out of a common building type--one that is not generally associated with high design standards. The design addresses this standard service amenity by viewing it from a fresh perspective and taking it to a higher level where it can have a positive influence on its surroundings. Primarily, the building provides 900 parking spaces. In addition, the structure offers a visually memorable arrival point and gateway to the new Civic Center, street-level retail and café amenities, spectacular views of the Pacific Ocean and the city, a garden, and a sense of personal safety.

The building works efficiently at four different levels:

AN URBAN SOLUTION

The varied amenities incorporated into the Parking Structure allow the designed mass to function beyond its service capacity. The four sides of the building acknowledge the individual urban contexts, thus serving as a fully designed urban presence. Small retail spaces at the pedestrian level expand the building's civic edge, creating a destination as well as a gateway. A lively café on the main plaza terrace animates the pedestrian flow into and out of the heart of the Civic Center. The Zen garden and a commissioned work of art highlight both the inside and the outside of the building, making it more hospitable to the community than an ordinary parking structure.

A SUSTAINABLE STRUCTURE

The building functions as an efficient sustainably designed structure. Photovoltaic panels on the roof and laminated to three façades of the built mass provide much of the building's energy needs. The array of angled photovoltaic cells serves to accentuate the skyline and provides a memorable symbol for the Civic Center.

All façades allow natural ventilation and illumination to enter all parking floors. The ceilings are painted white to maximize the quality of light and airiness. Multicolored glass panels welcome day-lighting into the Parking Structure, decreasing the amount of artificial light that is generally needed for this type of building, while adding a glowing beauty to the interior by day and a luminous exterior by night. The structure becomes a sensor and vessel of light, colors, and patterns, ranging from transparent to translucent.

城市的入口

最近完成的市中心总体规划标明了位于第四大街和新奥林匹克大道上的通向一个新区的城市入口，该新区包括修复过的老市政厅、法庭以及新公共安全大楼。这个新的停车场就被设想成这组市政建筑四部分中的另一个完整部分，将在地上的六层和地下的两层里提供900个停车位，并在视觉上将不同的建筑整合在一起。除此之外，设计小组还面临着要为城市提倡的可持续设计树立榜样的挑战，同时，还要加强城市肌理并为公众提供便捷。

这个项目面临的挑战之一就是要跳出普通的建筑形式——通常不是高设计水准的建筑形式。这个设计展现了一个高标准的服务设施——从一个新鲜的角度看待它，并且更进一步，使它对它的周围施加一种积极的影响。这个建筑主要提供900个停车位。除此以外，该构造还创造一个视觉上令人难忘的市中心入口，同时还提供街道平面的零售和咖啡馆等设施、壮丽的太平洋和城市的景色以及一个花园、一种私密的安全感。

这座建筑在以下四个不同方面起到了有效的作用：

城市解决方案

在这个停车场中融合了各种便捷设施，使这座建筑在超出其服务能力之外的范围发挥着作用。建筑的四个面都尊重各自的城市环境，也就是说它在城市中的存在是经过充分设计的。在人行道平面上的小零售空间延伸了建筑物的市民界面，在塑造了一个入口的同时也塑造了一个目的地。在主要广场平台上有一个有生气的咖啡馆，它激活了进出市中心内部的人流。禅花园和受托创作的艺术作品则强调了建筑物的室内和室外，使它比起一个普通的停车设施来说对社区显得更加友善。

一座可持续性的建筑

这是一座发挥了有效作用的可持续建筑。屋顶上和三个立面上覆盖的光电板提供了该建筑所需要的很多能量。成角度排列的光电单元强调了天际轮廓线，同时也成为市中心一个值得注意的标志。

所有立面都保证自然通风和自然照明进入各层停车场。天花板被涂成白色以使光线和通风质量最优化。彩色的玻璃板将日光引入停车场的构造，减少了在这种建筑中通常需要的人工照明，同时，在白天为室内带来鲜艳的光芒，而在晚上呈现一个发光的外立面。这个构造成为从透明到半透明的光线、色彩和图案的感应器和容器。

INCREASED SAFETY AND SECURITY

The design incorporates several features that provide comfort, safety, and security for users of the Parking Structure. Parking is organized on eight floors, accessed via a centralized circulation spine. The elevator core and stairs are positioned with respect to the two major pedestrian paths in the Civic Center campus. Access and exits have been consolidated at two corners of the building which serve as a control point to efficiently channel both pedestrian and vehicular traffic toward destination points. The reflective surface of the façade can be illuminated after sunset to glow as a shimmering curtain, providing defensible space through a pleasing ambient light.

A UNIQUE PRESENCE: MATERIAL PALETTE

The design does not disguise the utilitarian nature of the building, but instead seeks to celebrate this aspect as part of the design aesthetic. Automobiles, from their colors, types, and movement, are integrated as elements in the overall design strategy. The design solution uses colored laminated glass channels, photovoltaic panels, ribbed pre-cast concrete panels, and steel mesh to render a unique civic presence. The dynamic integration of these materials makes the structure function as an urban curtain in its vibrant context.

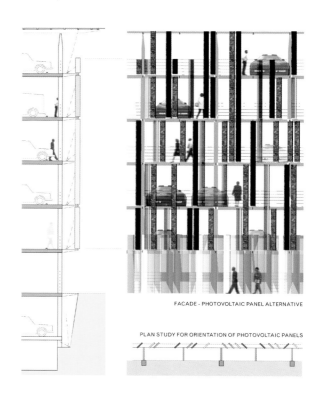

FACADE - PHOTOVOLTAIC PANEL ALTERNATIVE

PLAN STUDY FOR ORIENTATION OF PHOTOVOLTAIC PANELS

above left and center: lighting study mockup of colored laminated glass channels

左上及中间：彩色玻璃板采光照明研究模型

增强的安全感

该设计包含了几个为使用者提供舒适和安全的特性。停车被安排在八层楼内,通过一个集中的交通核到达。电梯和楼梯间的位置考虑了市中心的两条主要人行道。在建筑的两个转角,入口和出口合并成为有效的控制点,运送行人和机动车到达他们的目的地。反光的外表面在日落之后可以被点亮从而成为一片闪烁的帘幕,发散的宜人的漫射光形成一个防御空间。

独特的外观: 材料格网

我们的设计并没有掩盖这座建筑的实用性,而是试图把这一点作为设计美学的一部分。汽车的颜色、种类和运动都作为元素被整合到整体设计之中。设计方案运用彩色玻璃板、光电板、肋状预制混凝土板以及钢筋网来表现一种独特的城市外表。这些材料的动态结合使这个构造在充满活力的环境中成为城市的一张幕布。

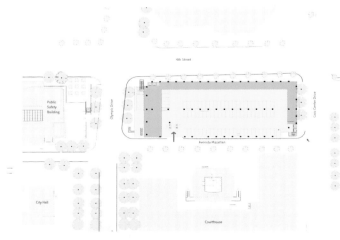

CLARICE SMITH PERFORMING ARTS CENTER

CLARICE SMITH表演艺术中心

The Performing Arts Center evolved as an articulated academic village with a rich multiplicity of scales, paths and environments. It is unique in its programmatic aspirations. Academic departments for music theater and dance are combined with an array of practice and performance venues and an arts library, in a mix that balances the needs and domains of departments, of the campus and of the region. A key design challenge was to create departmental identities that could co-exist with the large-scale reading of the project as a campus and regional serving center. The whole comprises over 300,000 square feet and occurs on the periphery of the campus, flanked by massive parking areas, the stadium and high-rise student housing.

A CAMPUS WITHIN A CAMPUS
The early planning for the center established the concept of shaping a series of departmental courtyards to establish individual identity and domain. Each of these is oriented along one of the adjacent campus axes. At the confluence of these domains, a dominant axis connects from a public entry plaza, flanked by the arts library, through an interior street and out to a naturally sloped amphitheatre.

RETHINKING CAMPUS LANGUAGE
The building developed formally as an assemblage of Platonic forms that express the complexity and hierarchy of internal ritual and function. This expression of taut, skinned, volumetrically clear solids became a primary way of harmonizing a modern formal language with the existing Georgian campus architecture. The language of white windows and porches was reinterpreted as a family of white metal light scoops or lanterns and a series of simple metal porches and bays.

The forms are quiet toward the periphery where simple porches and stair towers reinforce entry. They build up the large form of the major concert hall. For economy, most forms derive from cubic geometry with flat roofs, but special roofs rise up for iconic and programmatic reasons. Courtyards, allées and passages are shaped as positively configured open spaces; vessels for movement and habitation.

GATHERING HALLS
Along the "main street" of the complex, each of seven major performance venues has a presence. Each venue is conceived as a uniquely shaped object or pavilion with individual entry porticos. The group becomes a family of forms connected and gathered by stairs, walls and balconies, which animate the path. Entries to a café, garden, library and exhibition space further enliven this central armature to create a multi-dimensional social and cultural venue. Here a diverse community interacts in serendipitous or programmed gatherings.

MULTI-SENSORY SHAPING
Our most powerful inspirations for these forms were light and sound.

A series of lanterns, clerestories and bays illuminate practice spaces, performance halls and paths. Daylight is typically brought in high, and bounced through expressed structure, finally to wash the walls in soft and shifting light. Since the building has opened, this changing, complex environment has become a powerful magnet for social and academic interaction. At night, the syncopated reading of the lanterns provides a beguiling intimation of the creative flux within.

这个表演艺术中心逐渐成为一个有着丰富的尺度、道路和环境的教学村，尤其独特的是它对计划性的追求。音乐、戏剧和舞蹈等教学系所与一排练习、表演场所和一个文科图书馆组合在一起，在系所、校园以及地区的需求和领域之间取得平衡。设计所面临的一个关键挑战，是在营造出各系所的特性的同时，还要让这个项目从整体上看成为校园和地区的服务中心。这个项目占地27,871平方米，位于校园的外围，在其侧面是大块的停车场、体育场和高层学生住宅。

校园中的校园
这个中心的早期规划概念，是要形成一系列系所的庭院，以确立各单体的个性和领域感。每个庭院都朝向一条附近的校园轴线。在这些领域汇合的地方，一条支配性的轴线从一个公共入口广场开始，路过图书馆，穿过一条室内街道，再穿出到达一个自然倾斜的圆形剧场。

对校园建筑语言的再思考
建筑正式地发展为一个理想的形式，表达了内部习惯和功能的复杂性和层次。这种表面紧凑、体量清晰的实体表达成为协调现代形式语言和原有的乔治亚风格的校园建筑的主要方式。白色窗户和门廊的语言被转译成一类白色金属采光口或天窗，以及一系列简单的金属门廊和隔间。

外围处的形式是宁静的，简单的门廊和楼梯塔强调了入口。它们形成了主音乐厅的宏大形式。出于节约、简洁考虑，大多数形式都从平屋顶的几何立方体衍生而来，但有一些特殊的屋顶为了突出标志性和计划性而向上升高。庭院、小径和走道成为具有清晰形状的开放空间，也成为活动和居住的容器。

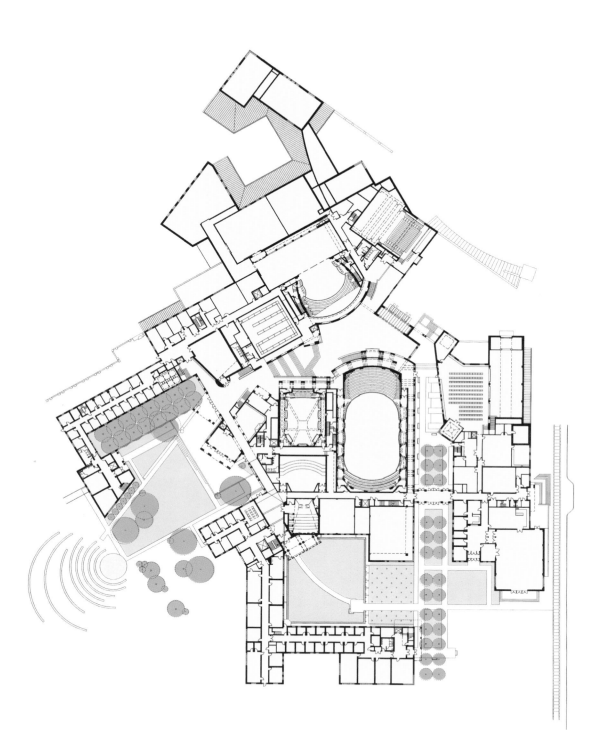

Sound was both a powerful and a subtle influence: volumes and proportions of spaces established acoustic qualities, which were further enhanced by material choices.

Sight and sound were also critical ways of shaping the major halls. Working with our clients, Theater Projects (theater) and Larry Kirkegaard (acoustics), we explored the unique characteristics that express the essential possibilities of each space.

The dance theater is muscular and direct in both shape and structure, yet daylight and color give it a lively and unpredictable quality.

The 650-seat theater is extraordinarily intimate: richly detailed and colored in warm dark woods and colors that embrace the audience yet direct focus on the performers.

The recital hall is shaped to be comforting and elegant; flexible enough to allow for small events, but ceremonial enough to honor the accomplishments of students in performance.

The steeply pitched roofs and expressed structure of the 1150-seat concert hall produce a bold, tectonic and inspirational space. In section this hall is shaped both for acoustic reflections and for the diffusion of light. Light enters through clerestory bays and is softened through layered walls, which also support audience and technical balconies. In plan the house is shaped to enhance the close communal experience of music and to allow for a sense of intimacy, whether partly or fully occupied. This is, in the end, an instrument for sound, light, meditation and community.

集会大厅
在这个综合体的"主街"两侧，排列着7个主要的表演场所。每个场所都被构想成一个有单独入口门廊的独特形式。这个组团成为一系列由楼梯、墙面和阳台相连的形式，由此激活了这条街道。通向咖啡厅、花园、图书馆和展览厅的入口进一步为这个中央骨架增添了活力，创造了一个多维的社会、文化场所。在这里，偶然的或经过计划的集会促成了社团的互动。

复合感官造型
我们在这些形式中最有力的灵感是光线和声音。

一系列的天窗、通风窗和天井照亮了练习场所、表演厅和走道。日光通常从高处进来，在明确的结构上来回反射，最终以柔和变幻的光线浸染墙壁。该建筑开放以来，这个不断变化的复杂环境变成了一个十分有吸引力的社交和教学互动场所。夜晚，天窗的切分节奏则诱惑性地暗示了内部创造性的流动感。

声音是一种既有力又很微妙的影响：空间的体积和比例决定了其声学特性，对材料的选择又将此声学特性提高。

光线和声音也是塑造主要大厅形式的重要方法。在与我们的客户——剧院项目方以及负责声学工程的Larry Kirkegaard的合作过程中，我们探索了表达每个空间的重要可能性的独特性质。

舞蹈舞台在形状和结构上都是有力的、直接的，同时，日光和色彩赋予它一种活泼且不可预知的性质。

有650个座位的剧院极具亲和力：温暖的深色木料有着丰富的细节和色彩，包围着观众，同时聚焦于表演者。

朗诵厅的形式塑造是舒适而优雅的，既具有一定的可变性以适于小型活动，同时又具有一定正式性，可以用来举行学生才艺颁奖典礼。

有着1,150个座位的音乐厅的陡峭坡度屋顶和明确的结构创造了一个大胆的、构造感强的且能唤起灵感的空间。从剖面上看，这个音乐厅同时考虑了声学反射和光线的传播。光线由天窗进入，通过支撑着观众席和包厢的层层墙面而变得柔和。从平面上看，这个建筑的形式增强了密切的音乐共鸣体验，并部分地或完全地营造了一种私密性。总之，这是一个服务于声音、光线、默想和团体的装置。

JOSEPH A. STEGER STUDENT LIFE CENTER

JOSEPH A. STEGER 学生生活中心

The Joseph A. Steger Student Life Center and the renovated Swift Hall are part of a new spine of campus activity organized along major pedestrian and topographic paths. The project is part of a multi-building "Main Street" planned collaboratively within a campus master plan by Hargreaves Associates. It is anchored at one end by Gwathmey Siegel's Tangeman Center and at the other by a new student recreation center designed by Morphosis. The Joseph A. Steger Student Life Center links the two along a thin curving site, traversing nearly six hundred feet in length and 55 feet of vertical drop.

The dense mix of academic, social and retail uses provide the community with a district of activity and urbanity not found within most university campuses.

ARC OF INTERACTION
The Center evolved as a vessel for movement and interaction. It traverses the site as a long slender form, which encourages parallel movement along a south-facing arcade. Student amenities and organizations have identities and entries along the arcade. The most active day/night uses, such as cafés and computer labs, are located at street level. Key paths of campus movement are reinforced though perpendicular cuts, literally short cuts through the building. A series of "found spaces" to the north are shaped as social places between the new building and existing buildings. To the west a covered atrium is formed between the Center and the older Swift Hall.

BODY LANGUAGE
This collection of spaces adjacent to buildings provides a diversity of domains in which to gather, perch, and move. They celebrate the pleasures of topographic movement and present a wide range of scales, thus heightening one's kinesthetic awareness.

The Center itself is a single-loaded building with social corridors along the south side. These recapitulate the movement of the arcade below and are animated by bays for informal gathering. Social stairs are day lit and become focal points for orientation and movement. The building form and fenestration frame, and are animated by, the activities within. Bays, galleries and arcades speak of the dynamic academic and social energy of the place.

TECTONICS OF EARTH AND SKY
The Center is built of simple, direct construction. It meets and merges with the earth though a combination of cast-in-place concrete and brick at the arcade. A light zinc and glass skin emphasizes horizontal movement and reflects the sky. Metal sunscreens protect the major south-facing gathering spaces. A program of boldly colored signage identifies and animates the social role of the building. The Center connects to the campus at multiple scales though axial movements, framed views, and positively configured open spaces.

A richness of habitation arises, in part, from the diversity of scale of places between, adjacent to, and inside the buildings. These present an array of space, articulated enough to invite habitation, yet flexible and subtle enough for the participants to improvise and vary their scale and type of activity. From the window bay for one or two, to a quiet mews terrace, to the large enclosure of the atrium or sweep of the arcade, the inhabitant is engaged in a dynamic·interaction with the building and its greater campus setting.

Joseph Steger学生生活中心以及修复过的Swift Hall是一条新的校园活动主轴的一部分，这些活动被组织在主要人行道和地形道路旁。这个项目是一个复合建筑"主街"的一部分，"主街"的规划是与Hargreaves事务所所作的校园总体规划协同完成的。它的一端由Gwathmey Siegel设计的Tangeman中心固定，而另一端则由Morphosis设计的学生娱乐中心固定。Joseph Steger学生生活中心将两者沿着一个细长的曲线形地段联系起来，地段长183米，垂直方向上跨越了16.8米的落差。

教学、社交以及零售等功能的密集混合为这个社区赋予了一种大多数校园中很难找到的活力和城市性。

互动的圆弧
中心逐渐演变为一个运动与互动的容器。它以一种细长的形式穿过地段，这种形式促进了沿着一个朝南的拱廊的平行运动。学生服务设施和学生组织具有独特的个性，且沿拱廊有各自的入口。最有活力的24小时开放的功能体，比如咖啡厅和计算机房，位于街道层平面。校园运动的主要道路在纵截面——也就是建筑的短向截面中得到加强。北边的一系列"被找到的空间"被当作新建筑与原有建筑之间的社交空间。在西侧，一个有顶的中庭连接着该中心与较古老的Swift礼堂。

身体语言
这一系列建筑旁边的空间提供了多种场所，可以在其中聚集、小憩或是活动。它们展示了在地形中运动的乐趣，并体现了非常丰富的尺度，提高了人们的运动知觉。

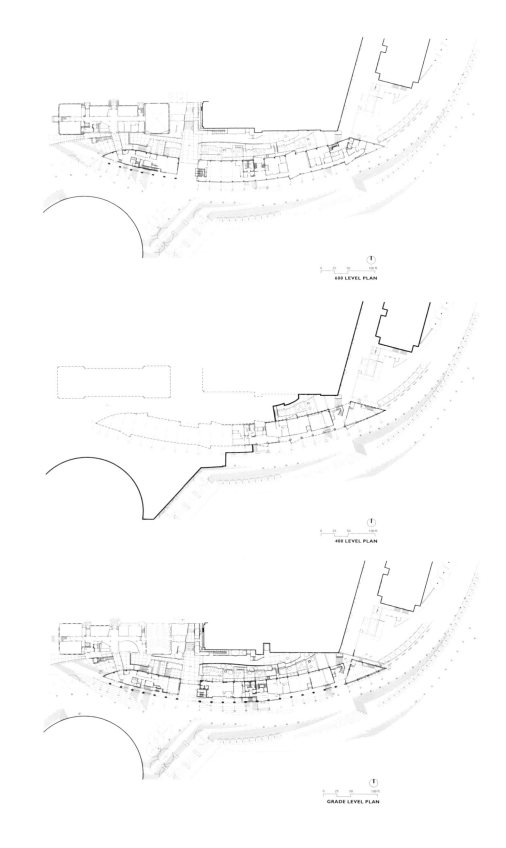

600 LEVEL PLAN

0 25 50   100 ft

400 LEVEL PLAN

0 25 50   100 ft

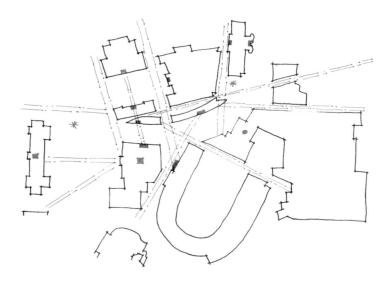

GRADE LEVEL PLAN

0 25 50   100 ft

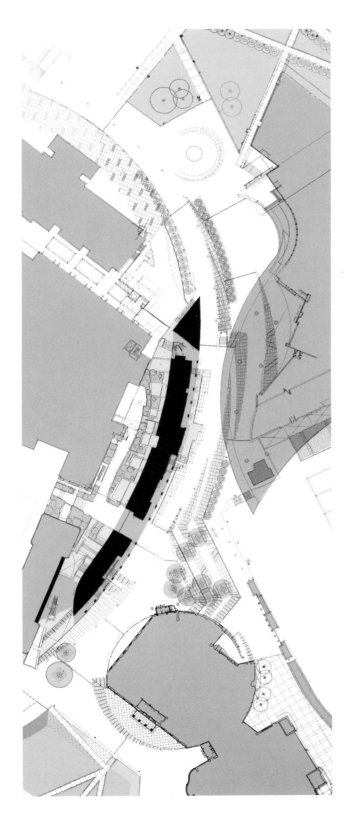

中心本身是一幢单边走廊的建筑，沿南侧有社交性的走廊。它们重演着下面的拱廊里的运动，一系列用于非正式聚会的隔间激活了它们。社交性楼梯在白天是被照亮的，成为定位和运动的焦点。建筑的形式和开窗限定了内部的活动，同时也由这些活动带来活力。隔间、连廊和拱廊表示了这个场所中动态的教学和社交活力。

天和地的构造
中心的结构是简单的、直接的，它与地面相接，并通过拱廊处现浇混凝土与砖的结合和地面融合起来。一个轻盈的锌和玻璃的面层强调了水平方向的运动，并反射出天空。金属的遮阳板为朝南的主要聚会场所遮阴。一系列有着显眼颜色的标志显示并激活了建筑的社会角色。

中心通过轴线性运动、框景以及形态明确的开放空间等在多种尺度上与校园相连。

环境的丰富性部分是由建筑之间、附近及其内部的场所的多重尺度衍生出来的。它们表示的这一系列空间，足够精致以吸引人群，但又足够灵活和敏感以使人们随兴地改变活动的规模和类型。从供一两个人使用的玻璃隔间，到一个安静的平台，再到中庭里的大型围合场地或是拱廊内的连续空间，人们动态地与建筑及其校园背景进行着交流。

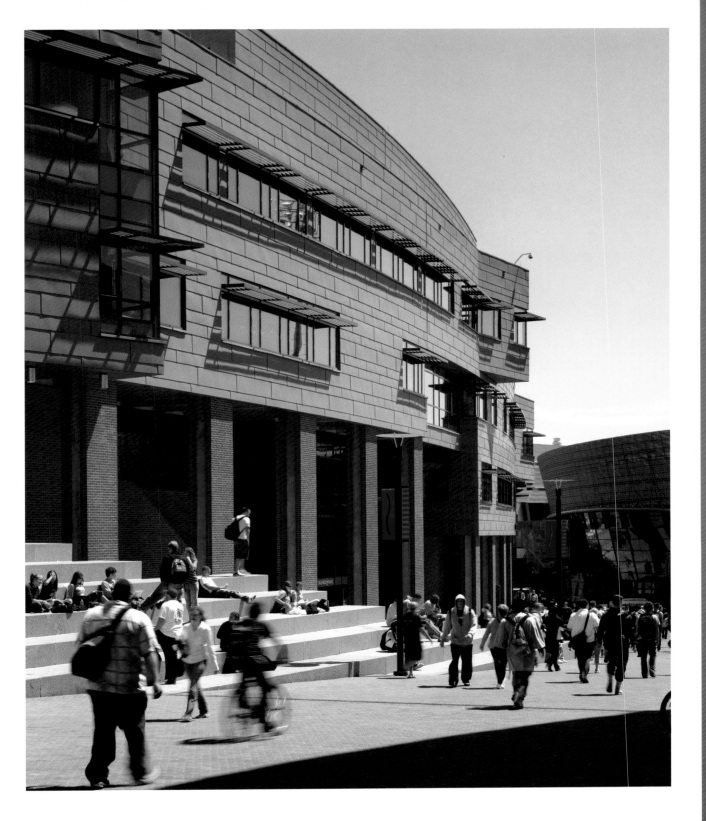

above: at the scale of the individual building, horizontal and vertical movement is designed to encourage informal interaction and socializing within "social stairs", arcades, and an atrium

上图：在这个独立建筑的尺度上，位于水平和垂直运动面的社会阶梯、拱廊、中庭都是为促进日常的社交互动而设计的

HORACE MANN ELEMENTARY SCHOOL

HORACE MANN小学

Diagonally across the street from the site of San Jose's new City Hall by Richard Meier is the neighborhood's new elementary school. In recognition of the context, the Community Redevelopment Agency called for a more substantial building than the School District's usual rock-bottom budget would provide, and were willing to put up the funds for it. The program for classes K-6 was also augmented to have a multi-purpose hall and other public-serving facilities, making the school and its playgrounds more of an all-around community center.

SIMULTANEOUS TRANSLATION
We wanted to have public design input, and the mixed Latino/Southeast Asian community showed up enthusiastically: our first tri-lingual design workshop! It was an unforgettable thrill to see that, after some initial head-scratching, teams of families and neighbors passionately argued in their various languages, and became deeply engrossed in laying out the school site using foam blocks and colored paper. They soon focused on practical issues like preserving open space for play areas, and enclosing outdoor spaces for security and control. Indeed, open space versus building was a challenging dilemma on the three-acre site.

LAW OF THE INDIES
Central San Jose had been laid out according to the Law of the Indies, the historic Spanish Colonial planning code that called for decorum and careful proportion in the arrangements of new towns. We wanted the school to have an analogous sense of order in the way that buildings framed public space in the half-city-block campus. After many alternatives we came to a three-story building scheme which, like some of the work-shop designs, hugs the northern edge of the site, partly screening the mass of a taller parking structure across the street. The school library and the multi-purpose hall hold the corners along East Santa Clara Street, framing a front garden around an enormous redwood tree. Rooftop play areas and outdoor circulation galleries are linked to the ground by sculptural, open stairways, making the building circulation system almost entirely visible from the central courtyard.

CIVILITY WITHOUT PRETENSE
The civic character of the school, a quality not emphasized in the school district's recent campuses, was realized by playing up the scale of the multi-purpose hall, library, and three-story classroom wing, and by using modest but durable materials—ground-face colored concrete block for exterior walls and sloped roofs and upper wall panels of metal. Most importantly, the school's varied open spaces are finely delineated with canopy-covered walks, allees of trees, solid masonry walls, and the building walls, giving character and significance to all parts of this urban campus.

在里查德·迈耶为圣何塞所作的巨大的新市政厅地段的斜对面，是周围地区的新建造的小学。出于对周边环境的认识和尊重，社区改造委员会提倡建造一座比一般校园最低预算所能承担的更为坚固的建筑，并愿意为之筹集资金。原来只包含幼儿园到六年级教室的任务书也得到扩张，增加了一个多功能厅以及其他公共服务设施，使这个学校和它的活动场更多地成为一个综合的社区中心。

同声传译
我们想让公众参与设计，这得到了拉丁美洲和东南亚社团的热心回应：这是我们第一个使用三种语言的设计讨论小组！我们非常激动地看到，在最初的一些摩擦之后，家庭、邻居形成的组团热心地用不同的语言进行讨论，并开始全神贯注地用泡沫塑料块和彩色图纸安排起学校的布置来。他们很快地关注到实质性的问题，比如保留开放空间以形成玩耍区域，以及把室外空间围合起来以保证安全并方便控制。确实，开放空间和建筑之间的权衡对于一块12,140平方米的地段来说是一个困难的选择。

INDIES法则
圣何塞中心区的布局遵守了"Indies法则"，这是个西班牙殖民时期的规划法则，它提倡在新城的规划中注重得体的礼仪和谨慎的比例。我们想让这个学校有一种类似的秩序感，便让建筑在这个占据一半城市街区的地段中围合出公共空间。在多种选择比较后，我们选定了一个三层楼的方案，和讨论小组里形成的一些方案一样，建筑紧靠地段的北边缘，部分地遮挡了街对面一个高大停车设施的体量。学校图书馆和多功能厅则占据了沿东圣克拉拉街的拐角，环绕着一棵巨大的红杉围合出一个前花园。屋顶活动场和室外交通走廊通过开放的雕塑楼梯与地面相连，使整个建筑的交通系统几乎都在中央庭院的视野之中。

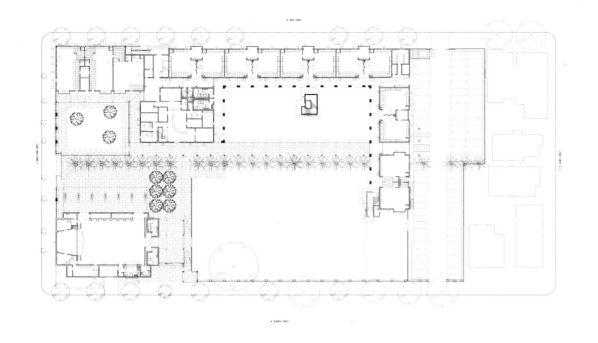

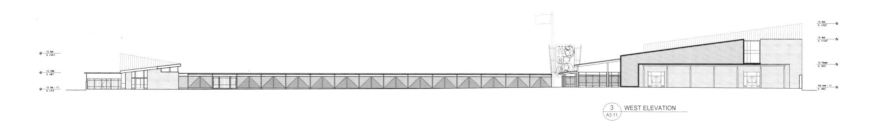

③ WEST ELEVATION
 A3.11

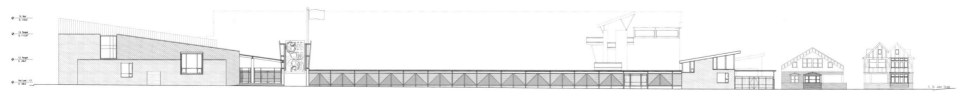

① EAST ELEVATION
 A3.11

远离虚伪的公民性

学校的市政特色在校区当前的校园中并没有作为一种良质得到强调，不过这次得到了实现——我们推敲了多功能厅、图书馆和三层教室楼的尺度，并运用普通但耐久的材料，比如外墙上的地表颜色的混凝土砌块、坡屋顶以及上层的金属板外墙面。最重要的是，学校多样的开放空间在有顶的步道、林荫小径、坚固的石墙以及建筑墙面的共同作用下得以精细地描绘，为这个城市园区的每一个部分带来个性与意义。

UNIVERSITY BOULEVARD

UNIVERSITY OF BRITISH COLUMBIA
VANCOUVER, CANADA
不列颠哥伦比亚大学，温哥华，加拿大

学院大道

The design for a new University Boulevard Neighborhood is the result of our winning submission for an international competition.

WEAVING CAMPUS AND COMMUNITY

Our design weaves the campus together, creating a vital nexus of community. This weaving occurs in social and academic realms, in space and time, and in the balance between buildings and landscape. Memorable places nurture interaction, connect to climate and context, and project the community into the global conversation. Buildings support a clear definition of the street and block structure of the campus. They reinforce linkages within the neighborhood and to adjacent districts. Positively configured open spaces support activities from serendipitous encounters to celebratory gatherings.

A FOCUS FOR CAMPUS LIFE

The confluence of memorable landscapes with diverse yet harmonious buildings and programs creates a powerful sense of entering and inhabiting a creative district. Key open space and buildings have clear identities yet weave a rich tapestry:

UNIVERSITY BOULEVARD

This landscaped promenade is paved with a rich woven pattern. A central rill reinforces the visual axis—a silver thread—while collecting rainwater. Under the elms, carpets of native grasses provide places for interaction.

THE ECO-STREAM

The eastern extension of University Boulevard is an ecological demonstration of water collection and purification using native species. A fountain at the intersection of the Main Mall acts as a source linking University Boulevard to the historic campus center.

The Bosque

The existing bosque becomes a more accessible weave of trees, paths, and activities.

DNA

Day-Night Atrium focuses on cultural, academic, and social activity. A woven canopy provides weather protection, water collection, and a technology-enhanced bosque.

UNIVERSITY SQUARE

Major open spaces converge at University Square where the weaving of paths and districts is celebrated. Here the historic elm protects the Goddess of Democracy.

SPACES BETWEEN

A carefully shaped set of secondary spaces creates quiet informal paths and courtyards. These spaces combine with roof gardens, providing a hierarchy of social spaces from public to private uses.

CONNECTIONS AND MOVEMENT

Pedestrians, bicycles, and vehicles are celebrated through clear expressions of gateway, threshold, path, and place. Buildings and landscape strengthen existing and new campus linkages.

LINKING TIME AND SPACE

Electronic infrastructure strengthens campus and global connections. Sciences and humanities can interact with video and performance arts through both hi-tech and high touch.

我们在一个国际竞赛中竞标成功，设计了这个新的校园大道及其周围的环境。

校园与社区的交织
我们的方案把校园编织在一起，形成了紧密的社区联系。这种编织发生在社交和学术范围中，发生在空间和时间中，还发生在建筑与景观的平衡之中。令人难忘的空间促进了互动，与气候和周围环境建立了联系，并把社区引入全球性的对话中。建筑提供了街道的明确定义和校园的街区结构。他们加强了与周围环境和附近街区的联系。形态明确的开放空间里进行着各种活动，从偶然的邂逅到庆祝性集会。

校园生活的焦点
令人难忘的景观，以及各自不同又互相协调的建筑和各种活动融合在一起，营造出一种进入并居住在一个创造性区域的感觉。主要的开放空间和建筑有明确的特性，同时又编织成一幅丰富的织锦。

校园大道
这条景观性质的散步道的铺装呈现出丰富的编织图案。中间的一条小溪加强了视觉轴线——一条银色轴线，同时收集雨水。在榆树下，大片本土草坪提供了交流互动的空间。

生态溪流
校园大道向东的延伸展示了运用当地物种进行的水收集和净化。在主商业街（Main Mall）处的交叉口，一座喷泉将校园大道与原来的校园中心联系起来。

树丛
原有的树丛变成了一个更易到达的树木、道路和活动的交织体。

BUILDING AND PROGRAM
The entire ground level is programmed for maximum activity and transparency. Clear entries, bays, terraces, and social spaces animate the street and express the rich habitation within.

FLEXIBILITY
Buildings are designed for current uses while accommodating long term flexibility. They are constructed with high bay floors and generic column spacing.

MATERIALITY AND TECTONICS
Materials are expressed for their inherent beauty, weaving the new neighborhood into the existing fabric. Materials connect to precedents, place, and contemporary life.

HOUSING TYPOLOGIES
Housing is designed to accommodate varied needs (apartments, lofts, work/live). Units optimize daylighting and indoor-outdoor relationships.

SUSTAINABILITY
Our approach to sustainability fosters the long-term stewardship of resources. It employs low-tech intelligent site planning, climatic responses, and progressive initiatives. Demonstration projects manifest the intentions of sustainability and integrate these programs into the academic and social life of the campus.

IMPLEMENTATION
Our proposal grows out of urban and environmental principles, creating a vision for sustainable growth. Weaving campus and community allows for creative, flexible, and phased implementation. Each stage establishes a coherent and vibrant whole while fostering responsiveness to evolving opportunities of the UBC community.

全天候中庭(DNA)
全天候开放的中庭聚焦于文化、教学和社交活动。一个编织成的顶棚提供了风雨中的遮蔽所，收集了雨水，还拥有一个高科技的树丛。

校园广场
主要的开放空间汇集于校园广场，这里以道路和区域的交织闻名。在这里，老榆树下伫立着民主女神像。

过渡空间
一系列精心塑造的次级空间形成了安静的、非正式的道路和庭院。这些空间与屋顶花园一起，形成了从公共用途到私密用途的社交空间的层次。

above: view towards the Day-Night Atrium (DNA), transit entry, and University Square

上图：穿过整个校园广场，观全天侯开放中庭之景

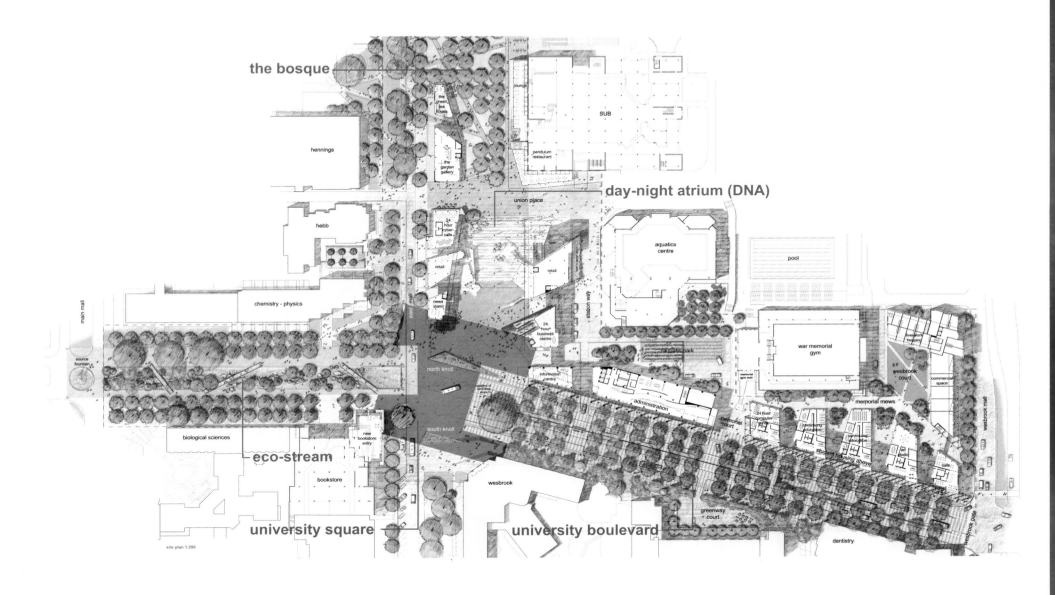

the bosque

day-night atrium (DNA)

eco-stream

university square   university boulevard

site plan 1:200

139

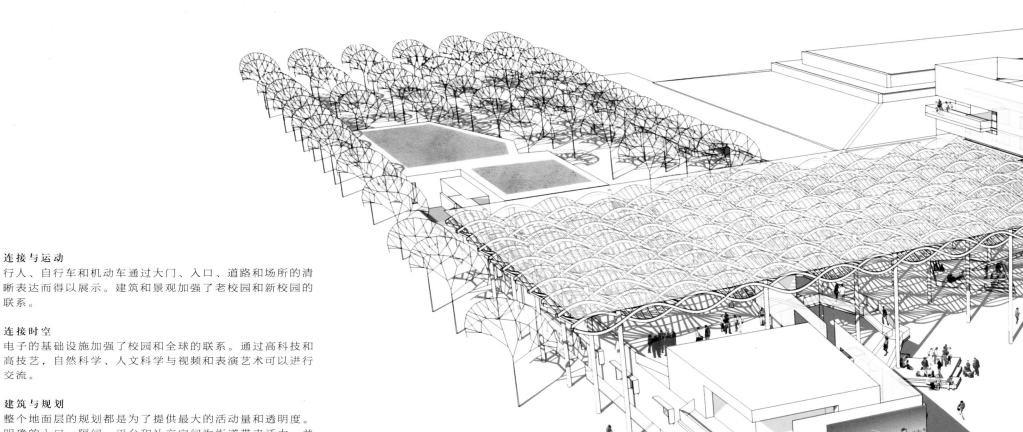

连接与运动

行人、自行车和机动车通过大门、入口、道路和场所的清晰表达而得以展示。建筑和景观加强了老校园和新校园的联系。

连接时空

电子的基础设施加强了校园和全球的联系。通过高科技和高技艺，自然科学、人文科学与视频和表演艺术可以进行交流。

建筑与规划

整个地面层的规划都是为了提供最大的活动量和透明度。明确的入口、隔间、平台和社交空间为街道带来活力，并表达出其中丰富的居住环境。

灵活性

建筑是为当前的用途设计的，同时也考虑到了长期使用的灵活性。它们由高大的空间和普通间距的柱网组成。

材料运用和构造学

材料将新的环境织入原有的肌理，表达了它们本身的内在美。材料的运用参考了惯例，并与特定场所和现代生活有关。

住宅类型学

住宅的设计包含了多种用途：公寓、阁楼工作室，工作/住宅混合等。住宅单元使日照和室内外联系最优化。

可持续性

我们实现可持续性的方法需要长期的资源管理。我们运用了低端技术——智能化场地设计，采用了对气候的应对，并且具有不断进步的进取心。示范工程表明了可持续性的意图，并把它们与校园的教学、社交活动联系起来。

实施

我们的方案来自于城市和环境的原则，为可持续性发展创造了一个前景。校园与社区的交织考虑到了创造性的、灵活的和阶段性的实施。每个阶段都建立起一个连贯而有活力的整体，同时，鼓励对校园社区内不断发展的机会作出回应。

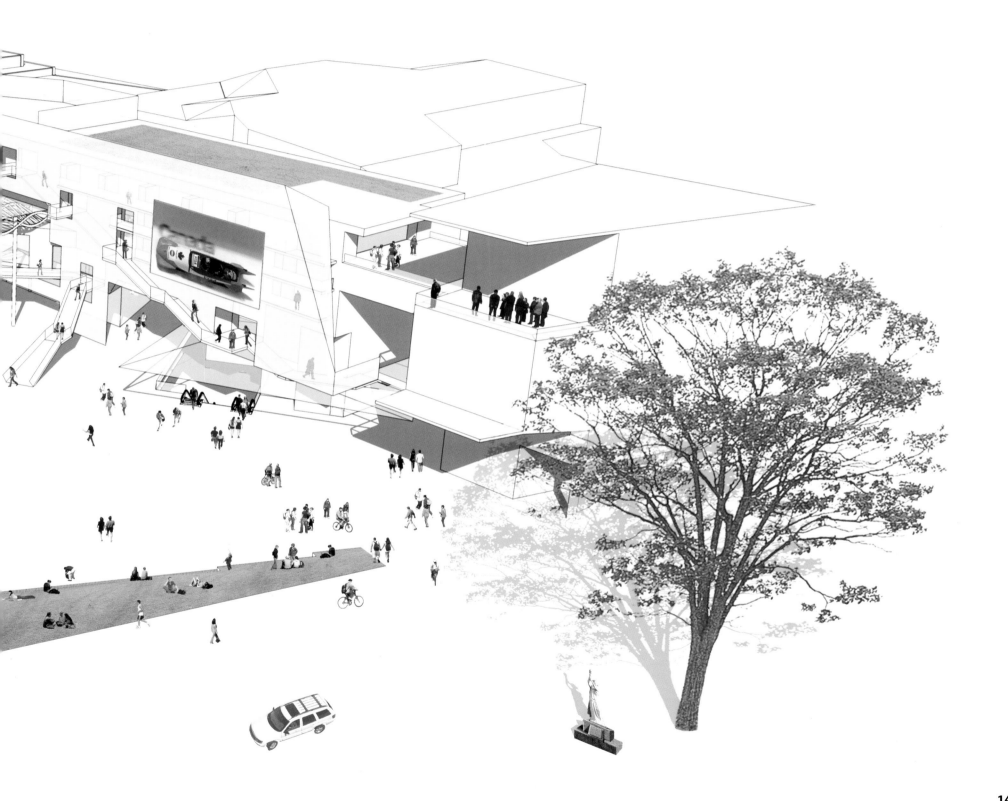

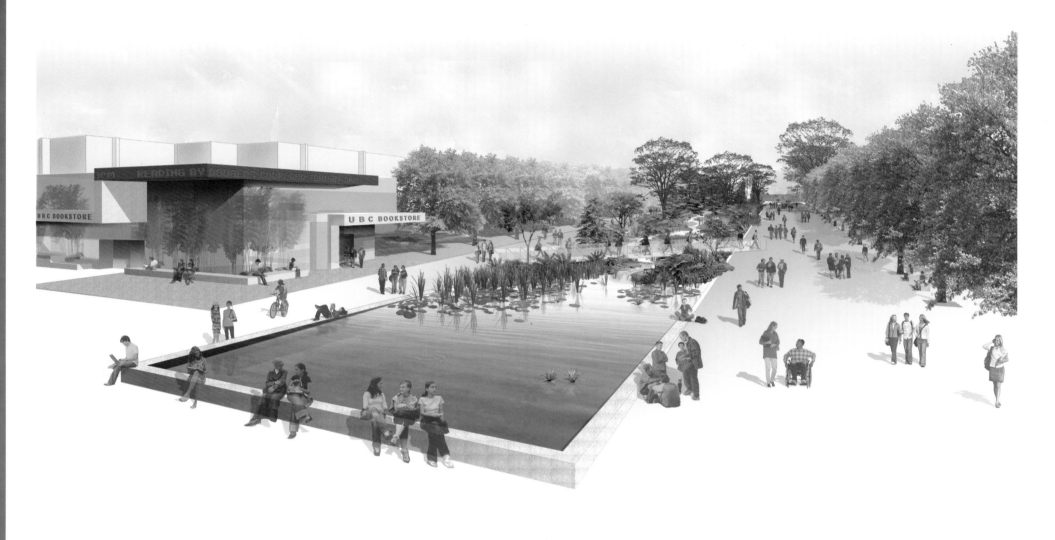

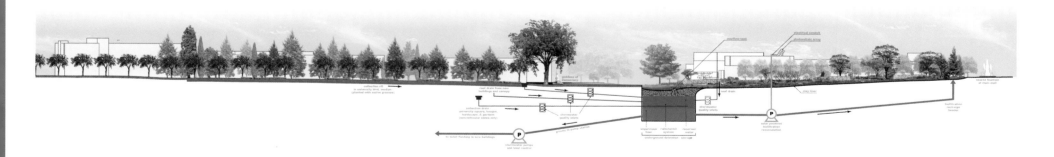

above: view towards Campus Main Mall, including Bookstore Addition and Eco-Stream

上图：校园主商业街，书店及生态溪流

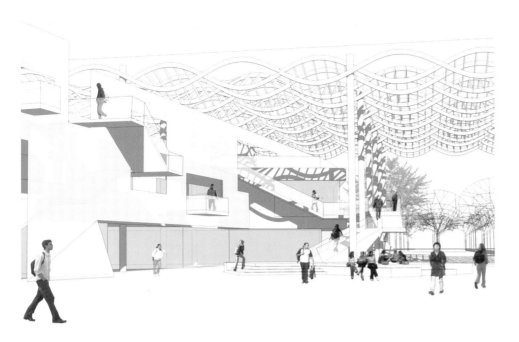

above: the 24-hour center offers social, educational, and cultural activities, with easy access to transit systems

上图：24小时中心提供社交，教育以及文化活动，并配有便捷的路径系统

above: the campus creates links between the administration/
cafeteria and laboratory buildings

上图：校园成为行政办公楼，咖啡厅和实验楼之间的连接

BIOTECHNOLOGY DEVELOPMENT CAMPUS

生物技术开发园区

This project for a leading international biotechnology firm is comprised of an analytical and process research laboratory, an administration building, and a cafeteria. These three facilities were interwoven and connected to an existing administration and laboratory building to give a stronger character and identity to this manufacturing campus.

The site near the eastern slope of the Rocky Mountains enjoys dramatic views across the nearby grasslands. The high, dry character of the regional landscape is energized by the powerful light of the Colorado sun.

Moore Ruble Yudell led multiple design teams in programming, concept design, and site planning, following an overall established master plan for the campus. From this effort emerged the design of three separate facilities and their linking structures. The design and construction was accelerated: from the start of the team's work until project completion lasted less than two years.

From programming through design, project goals were clarified, guided by the requirement to develop highly flexible facilities that would accommodate the firm's rapidly changing needs, efficiency, and environmental sensitivity. Energy savings through the use of heat-recovery and variable air volume systems, the appropriate use of natural light, the careful selection of materials and the development of a supportive working environment also guided the design effort.

The two-story laboratory building was developed with a two-corridor scheme that defines three linear bands of varying uses. Offices, interaction spaces and conference rooms are grouped along a sky-lit corridor on the side of the building that allows for these spaces to take advantage of mountain views to the west and provide an articulated public face to the entry. The middle, internal band provides laboratory and building support spaces. In order to keep sensitive equipment away from the solar gain of the hot western sun, we placed the laboratories on the east side of the building. Laboratory space is provided with natural light and highly flexible space, with all major services provided from the service corridor, allowing for flexible changes to research space. Also included, as a separate wing, is the Process Experimentation Laboratory that provides flexible, high technology materials laboratory space for the invention of new ways of manufacturing the company's products.

The administration building's design enhances its representational quality as the "front door" of the campus. Large scale vertical piers of precast concrete and stone accent the main façade. A variety of exterior wall systems are composed to respond to climatic concerns on the four different sides of the building.

这个为一个领先的国际性生物技术公司所做的项目，由三部分组成：一个分析和生产研究实验室、一个行政办公楼以及一个咖啡厅。这三部分互相交织在一起，并与一个原有的行政和实验楼连在一起，为这个制造业的园区赋予了一种强烈的性格特征。

地段邻近洛基山脉的东坡，享有附近草原的绚丽景致。该区域景观的高原干旱特征在科罗拉多的猛烈日照的作用下得到加强。

MRY在遵循着一个事先确立的园区总体规划的基础上，领导着多个设计小组，包括设计策划、概念设计及场地设计。在这种努力下，产生了包括三个单独设施及其连接构造的设计方案。设计和建造的过程是十分迅速的：从小组开始工作到工程完成，只用了不到两年。

从策划开始，贯穿整个设计，项目的目标是清晰的：按要求开发高度灵活的设施，以适应公司快速变化的需求、效率以及环境敏感度。另外，还有一些因素指导了设计：通过废热重新利用和可变气体容积系统实现节能，对自然光的合理运用，对材料的明智选择，以及一个良好工作环境的发展。

两层高的实验楼被设计为一个双走道的方案，形成了三个具有不同功能的线性带。办公室、互动空间和会议室被安排在一个天光走廊的一侧，从建筑的这一侧可以看到西边的山景。这几个房间形成了一个精致的公共入口外观。位于中间的内部功能带容纳了实验室和建筑供应空间。为了避免敏感的仪器受到夕晒热量的影响，我们把实验室安排在建筑的东侧。我们为实验室提供了自然光和高度灵活的空间，考虑到研究空间的灵活变化，所有的服务都由服务走廊提供。此外，还有作为单独一翼的生产实验室，它提供了灵活的高科技材料实验室空间，用于发明公司产品的新制造方法。

行政办公楼的设计增强了它作为园区"前门"的代表性。竖向的大型预制混凝土和石头的支柱强调了主立面。建筑外墙系统的多样性是为了应答建筑在四个方向上不同的气候方面的考虑。

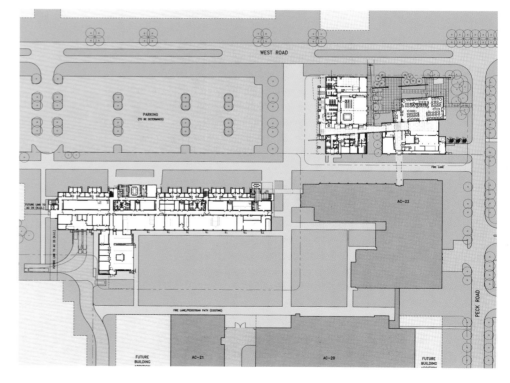

bottom right: site plan with laboratory building, administration building, and cafeteria

右下：实验楼，行政楼以及咖啡厅的平面图

above: laboratory building 上图：实验楼

148

above: administration building and details

右下：行政楼及细部

above: cafeteria and servery 上图：咖啡厅及服务区 **149**

MIT SLOAN SCHOOL OF MANAGEMENT

MASSACHUSETTS INSTITUTE OF TECHNOLOGY
CAMBRIDGE, MASSACHUSETTS, USA
麻省理工学院，剑桥，马萨诸塞州，美国

MIT斯隆商学院

This design effort involved planning for the phased growth of key academic elements, which currently inhabit a compact and somewhat incoherent district at the east end of the campus. Planning spans scales and issues, from the clarifying of faculty research clusters to the shaping of clear building and open space relationships.

The relationships between academic departments will be strengthened, as will the connections to the greater MIT campus and to the city of Cambridge.

UNDERSTANDING PLACE
The MIT Campus is part of a dense urban fabric, which is woven into the historic development of Cambridge and metropolitan Boston. The campus occupies an isosceles triangle with a long east-west axis aligned along the Charles River and a short north-south axis defined by Massachusetts Avenue. The intersection of two historic street grids underlies the campus form.

A study led by Laurie Olin resulted in the "Framework Plan," which identified patterns of campus development and clarified principles for growth. Building on this, we identified key opportunities to strengthen visual, spatial, and social linkages between the growing eastern district and the Institute as a whole, as well as to the surrounding city of Cambridge and Boston across the Charles River.

The study area is densely impacted by utilities, dysfunctional buildings, surface parking, disaggregated open space, and minimal connections to the banks of the Charles River. At the same time, the campus requires the opportunity to phase development to a significantly higher density than now exists in the district and in much of the campus. By phasing the removal of secondary buildings with the denser development of carefully configured new mixed-use buildings, we proposed a major new campus-serving open space and a revived multi-departmental district.

SUPPORTING COMMUNITY
The culture of MIT is both informal and intense. Collaboration within and across disciplines is nurtured. At the Sloan School there is a strong initiative to encourage diverse and non-traditional forms of research and study. The intensity of the individual and group work dynamic makes it critical that the architecture support multiple interactions, from two individuals interacting, to whole departments meeting, to connecting to the campus community at large.

OF LOFTS AND LINKS
Our plan for the East Campus is organized around the shaping of major new campus open spaces. The new buildings act to frame those spaces as well as to incubate academic interaction. At the urban scale, major paths, new buildings, and open spaces are organized along the key axes of the campus and the city. Their form and spatial experience reference the intersection of the historic street grids.

The current plan accommodates a mix of academic and social spaces in more than 500,000 square feet in several phases. Some 200 units of housing can be accommodated in later phases to support long-term institutional goals.

我们的设计包括对一些重要的教学性元素的阶段性发展进行规划，这些元素目前处在一个紧凑且有些不连贯的区域内。规划涉及尺度问题，并提出一些解决方案，从精简整理教学研究机构到塑造清晰的建筑和开放空间的关系。

各教学系所之间的关系，以及它们与MIT校园以至剑桥市之间的关系将得到强化。

理解空间
MIT的校园是一种密集的城市肌理的一部分，这种肌理是与剑桥和大城市波士顿历史上的发展融合在一起的。校园位于一个等腰三角形的地段上，地段的东西向长轴平行于查尔斯河，而南北向短轴则由马萨诸塞大街确定。这两个历史街道格网的交叉点成为校园形式的基础。

一项由Laurie Olin领导的研究确定了"框架规划"，确定了校园发展的模式，并阐明了其增长的原则。在这个前提下，我们抓住关键的机遇，以加强不断增长的东区与学院整体之间，以及与剑桥、河对岸的波士顿之间的视觉、空间和社会性联系。

教学区域现在拥挤地充斥着公共设施、功能混乱的建筑、地表停车以及分散的开放空间，并且与查尔斯河岸的联系极少。与此同时，校园要求将密度逐步提高，直至大大超出该区域以及校园内大部分地方的现存密度。我们拆除了次级建筑，在更高的密度上发展了精心塑造的新的混合功能楼，这样就形成了一个为校园服务的主要新开放空间，复兴了多系所区域。

The Phase One building is organized as a horizontally and vertically integrated community. The first two floors accommodate instructional and social spaces and function as campus and departmental links. They connect continuously to a strongly figured entry court and to the river-facing quad. They allow for linkages to a matrix of existing academic buildings. A series of loft-like towers rise from these more public spaces. They are configured to encourage interaction in optimally sized faculty clusters oriented to different areas of research. These can, in turn, link horizontally through "soft boundaries" and vertically through social stairs.

Through the shaping of path and place at multiple scales, the overall plan seeks to create a new multi-departmental focus for research, instruction, and community interaction. The clear new figure-ground plan should establish a strong connection to the greater campus and a vital presence at its eastern prow.

社团支援

MIT的文化是随意而热情的。学科内和跨学科的合作受到鼓励和支持。在斯隆商学院有一股强烈的进取心，鼓励多种非传统的研究、学习形式。个人和团体工作的强度，使建筑必须支持多种互动以增强社团感。必须鼓励多种尺度

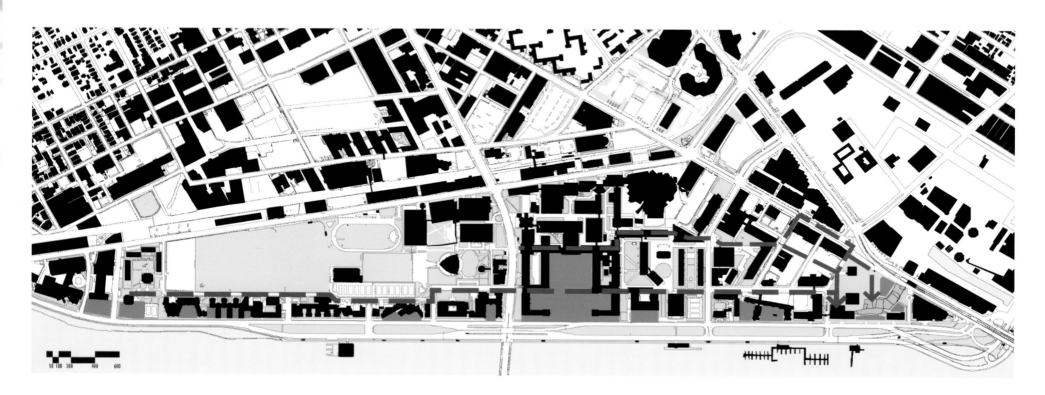

的社团，从两人间的交流到全系性会议，再到与校园社区之间的联系。

阁楼与接点

我们为东校区作的规划是围绕着主要新校园开放空间的塑造来进行的。新建筑限定了这些空间，同时也促进了教学交流。在城市的尺度上，主要道路、新建筑和开放空间被组织在校园和城市的主要轴线的两侧。它们的形式和空间体验令人回想起历史街道格网的交叉口。

现在的平面分成几个阶段，在46,450余平方米的面积中容纳了教学和社交混合空间。在以后的阶段中，将增加大约200个住宅单元，以达到学院的长期目标。

建筑的"第一阶段"被构想为一个横向和竖向相融合的社区。首层和二层是教学和社交空间，起到校园和院系中的联系作用。它们连贯地通向一个形式强烈的入口庭院和面向河的中庭。考虑到了与现有的一片教学楼的联系。

一系列阁楼状的塔从这些公共性较强的空间中上升出来。它们的形式塑造是为了鼓励教学机构中的交流互动，这些教学机构具有理想的规模，容纳了不同领域的研究。这些阁楼本身又通过"柔性边界"进行横向联系，通过社交性楼梯进行竖向联系。

通过在多种尺度上对道路和空间的塑造，整个平面试图为研究、教学和社区互动创造一个新的多系所的焦点。这个清晰的新图底关系平面将与校园建立起强烈的联系，并使得从其东端看去是一个有活力的外观。

LAW-BUSINESS CONNECTION

法学与商学院综合楼

The new Law-Business Connection (LABC) at the University of California, Berkeley is a building that physically and academically bridges the programs of the Haas School of Business and the Boalt School of Law.

Located on a sloping site at the northeast edge of campus, the new LABC creates multiple links and passages between law and business in the north-south direction. In the east-west direction it terraces down and works with the landscape to create a sensitive relationship to the residential scale to the east and to optimize views to San Francisco Bay to the west.

The building is developed as two academic wings with a series of shared conference and social spaces bridging the wings. Each academic wing can thus have an identity and can be closely associated with its respective professional school: Business to the north and Law to the south. Each wing supports faculty and graduate student research with a combination of classrooms, faculty offices, and flexible shared space for research centers, conference rooms, and outdoor terraces at each floor.

The shared central core of the building is focused around a three-story forum that encourages informal interaction and can be reconfigured to accommodate several hundred participants for formal presentations. This space is extended to a terraced garden to the east, which also allows for a broad range of activities and presentations. A café, a lecture hall, seminar rooms, and group study areas are arrayed in close adjacency to the forum to further support its flexible use. The forum and its support spaces are enhanced by technology which allows for interactive video communication on a local or global level. This focus for academic discussion and social interaction will become an important venue for regional and international participants and visitors.

The building is designed to be environmentally sustainable. Carefully integrated mechanical and structural systems reduce energy consumption while optimizing user comfort. The orientation of the major wings minimizes east and west heat gain while optimizing prevailing breezes and regional views. Exterior shading combines with interior "light shelves" to cut heat gain while increasing interior daylighting. Roof terraces are planted with native vegetation for water retention, air quality, and heat reduction. The central forum is defined by highly glazed walls with shading provided by a second layer of translucent glazing.

The building is experienced as an inviting and permeable set of places for meeting, study, and social interaction. Its connectivity to the landscape and transparency to the campus support the interdisciplinary academic mission.

加利福尼亚大学伯克利分校的新"法学与商学院综合楼"（LABC）在实体上和学术上都将Haas商业学院与Boalt法律学院的教学项目连接起来。

新LABC楼坐落于校园东北角的一个斜坡地段上，在南北向形成了法律与金融之间的多重连接与通道。东西方向上，它呈台地状下降，与景观一起，与东边的居住尺度之间形成了一种敏感的关系，而在西边则充分展现了旧金山湾的景色。

建筑形成了两个教学侧翼，由一系列共同的会议和社交空间连接起来。于是每个教学侧翼拥有自己的特性，并与它们各自的专业学院紧密联系起来：金融在北边，法律在南边。每个侧翼为教工和研究生的研究提供了一系列的教室、教工办公室，并在研究中心、会议室和每层室外平台上提供了灵活可变的共享空间。

建筑中央的共享核心的焦点是一个三层高的可以进行非正式互动交流的会场，它也可以经过改装，容纳几百人进行正式的演说。这个空间延伸到西边一个台地花园里，在这里也可以进行多种活动和演说。紧挨着会场排列着一个咖啡厅、一个讲演厅、一些讨论室和小组学习区域，进一步体现了其使用的灵活性。会场和它的附属空间采用了高科技，保证了地区或全球层次上的互动视频交流。这个学术讨论和社交互动焦点将成为当地的和国际的参与者、访问者的重要聚集场所。

top right and bottom: the forum is flexible to allow for both casual interaction and formal presentations

右上与右下：会场灵活多变，适合非正式的交流和正式的会议

建筑设计在环境上是可持续的。机械和结构系统被精心地
整合进来，不仅降低了能耗，也尽力提高了使用者的舒适
度。两个主要侧翼的走向减小了东西方向上吸收的热量，
同时充分利用了盛行风向的微风并展现了当地的景致。外
部的遮阳与内部的"反光板"一起减少吸热，并增加了室
内的自然光照。屋顶平台上种有本土植被以保存水分、改
善空气质量并减少热量。中央会场由大面积玻璃幕墙包
围，由另外一层半透明的玻璃提供了遮阳。

这座建筑被看做是一系列诱人且通透的场所，可用于会议、
学习以及社交互动。它与景观相联系，面向校园呈现出通透
性，承担了学科间的学术使命。

top: view of Law School wing entry; bottom: view of Business School wing with
Moore Ruble Yudell's Haas School of Business at left

上图：法学院侧翼全景
下图：商学院侧翼及左边摩尔乐伯约德Hass商业学院全景

157

above: the new Kaufman Family Garden Theater　　　　　上图：新建的Kaufman家族花园剧院

GLORYA KAUFMAN HALL

UNIVERSITY OF CALIFORNIA,
LOS ANGELES, USA
洛杉矶分校，加利福尼亚大学，美国

GLORYA KAUFMAN礼堂

TRANSFORMING A 1932 GYMNASIUM FOR UCLA'S DEPARTMENT OF WORLD ARTS AND CULTURE

This former women's gymnasium is one of the distinguished buildings framing UCLA's historic core campus. The building was badly damaged in a 1992 earthquake. The campus subsequently sought to leverage FEMA and state money for seismic, accessibility, and life safety upgrades to a much more ambitious goal: to restore the historic building and to transform it into a state of the art academic and performance venue for World Arts and Cultures (WAC). WAC was created in 1995, merging programs and resources from dance, world arts, folklore, mythology and material culture. It is a gathering of artists, educators, and students dedicated to developing interdisciplinary and multi-cultural creative work.

The project seeks to use building restoration, adaptive reuse, and new elements to create a flexible technology-enhanced home for all the departmental needs, within the constraints of the existing building and its small backyard. The approach to the building transformation involves both surgical interventions and broad planning initiatives.

CAMPUS CONNECTIONS

The new plan incorporates major connections to the expanding campus fabric. The original building had a formal front facing south and a perfunctory "back" facing north. Entry was through a formal portico and directly into a solid wall, behind which were locker rooms in a dark forest of columns.

While restoring the south portico and adding gentle accessible ramps, a new interior street is carved through the building, terminating in a new light filled two-story social stair. This connects to a new Garden Theater and establishes a new north entry adjacent to key campus pathways. A secondary path connects through the building east to a museum of cultural history and west to a vehicular drop-off point. At the intersection of these two paths, a departmental "town square" is flanked by classrooms, offices, and student social spaces.

NATURAL CONNECTIONS

A key element to the transformation of the building was opening it up to light, air, and landscape. The carefully incised openings bring light into the entire north side of the building and allow for visual and social connections to the new garden/theater. On the second floor, sub-standard, low-ceilinged practice spaces are converted to spacious dance studios with north clerestory light balancing light from the south.

STATE OF THE ARTS

Ethernet distribution and use of wireless data for theatrical controls and lighting makes this one of the most technology-enhanced arts facilities built to date. Multiple performance spaces, studios, and classrooms are linked to the A/V studio, allowing simultaneous broadcasting, recording, and production.

Key performance spaces include:

300 Seat Reconfigurable Main Theater

The original women's basketball court was both preserved and transformed. The architectural interventions are expressed as a kind of high-tech kit of parts, which are enormously flexible.

将1932年的女子健身房改造成世界艺术与文化系

原先的女子健身房是形成UCLA历史核心校园的著名建筑之一。在1992年的一次地震中这座建筑被严重地毁坏了。于是校园希望从联邦应急管理局（FEMA）寻求帮助，并申明资金将用于增加抗震性能、可到达性和生命安全，并达到一个更宏伟的目标：恢复原有建筑并将它改为世界艺术与文化系（WAC）的艺术教学和表演场所。WAC创建于1995年，从舞蹈、世界文学、民间传说、神话和实质陶冶训练等领域里合并了一些项目和资源。这是一个艺术家、教育者和学生的聚集，致力于发展跨学科和多元文化的创造性工作。

我们希望通过建筑的恢复、有适应性的再利用和新元素的介入，在原有建筑和它的小后院的限制下，创造出一个灵活的、科技先进的、能满足系内要求的"家"。对建筑进行的改造，不仅包括外观的调整，还包括宏伟的规划决心。

校园联接

新平面将主要流线与校园扩张的肌理合并起来。原来的建筑有个正式的朝南的正面和一个敷衍了事的朝北的背面。入口处通过一个正式的门廊直接进入一面坚硬的墙，墙后则是黑暗的密密麻麻的柱网中的衣帽间。

除保留南侧门廊并增加人性化无障碍坡道外，我们在建筑内嵌入了一条室内街道，其终点是一个光线充足的两层高的社交性楼梯。这条街道连接到一个新的"花园剧场"，建立了一个紧邻校园主干道的新的北入口。一条次一级的通道将建筑与东边的文化历史博物馆以及西边的机动车停靠点连接起来。在这两条通道的交点处，一个系内的"市镇广场"周围排布着教室、办公室和学生社交场所。

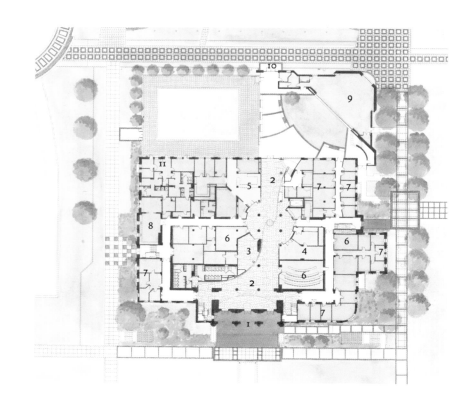

与自然的联系

建筑改造中一个非常重要的要素是让它向光线、空气和景观敞开。仔细切割出的开口将光线引入建筑的整个北部，同时提供了与新花园剧场的视觉和社交联系。在二层，原来不合标准、层高过低的练习空间被改为宽阔的舞蹈房，其中北向的天窗平衡着来自南方的光线。

艺术的姿态

以太网的分布和关于剧院控制和照明的无线数据，使这座科技最先进的文化建筑至今得以建成。多种表演空间、工作室与教室/视频音频工作室相连，保证了即时的广播、录音和创作。

主要的表演空间包括：

可重新改体的300座位主剧场：
原先的女子篮球场被保留下来，同时也被改造。建筑上的更改可以看作是一种高科技的具有高度灵活性的成套元件。在整个空间里，座椅可以移动，头顶可能悬浮着东西。舞台、观众、照明和景色的位置可以完全改变。空间可以形成多种形式，包括古希腊式舞台、古罗马式竞技场、日式歌舞剧舞台、凸出式舞台以及影剧院等。悬浮的包厢保证了整个大厅里的表演和练习的净跨使用。可滑动的百叶窗使原有的窗户可以覆以半透明的或不透明的面板。原先的结构被压缩并加强。

bottom: the new interior street connects student, faculty, and performance spaces

下图：新建的室内通道连接着学生，院系和剧场

Seats move and overhead suspensions can be achieved throughout the space. The stage, audience, lighting, and scenery locations can be radically reconfigured. The space can be configured in many forms including traditional proscenium, arena, kabuki stage, thrust stage, and studio theater. Suspended balconies allow clear-span use of the entire hall for performance or practice. Sliding shutters allow existing windows to be covered with translucent or solid panels. Existing structure is both expressed and reinforced.

Major new mechanical elements for ducts, wiring, house lights, and acoustic material are gathered into inverted "canoes". These perforated aluminum forms gather and temper the visual complexity of these services while clearly expressing the new elements floating in the historic space.

Garden Theater
This entirely new element expresses its contemporary presence while using a material palette that is sympathetic to its context. The 3,600-square foot pavilion serves as a combination theater stage, experimental performance space, lecture room, and dance studio. Full height sliding doors allow it to open in good weather. Smaller sliding doors allow for a visual and programmatic connection to the northeast at a major pedestrian intersection.

The project demonstrates how a contemporary program can be successfully combined with an historic building. Each revitalizes the other, in the same way that the creative collaborations of the students, faculty, and artists inform and energize one another.

above left: former second-floor gymasium; right: new second-floor theater in end-stage configuration

左上：原2楼的建身房
右图：新2楼的剧场，尽头为舞台

管道、电缆、观众席照明及声学设备所需的主要的新机械零件被聚集在反转的"独木舟"里面。这些穿孔的铝制设备聚集在一起，缓和了这些零件的视觉复杂性，同时，清晰地表达出悬浮于历史的空间中的新元素。

花园剧场：
这个全新的元素以一种现代的外观出现，同时运用了与环境和谐的材料色彩。这个3,344平方米的棚架成为剧场舞台、实验性表演场所、讲堂和舞蹈房的综合体。通高的滑动门在天气好时可以完全打开。在一个与人行道的主要交叉点处，一些更小的滑动门提供了与东北方向视觉和规划性的联系。

这个工程展示了一个现代项目如何成功地与历史建筑融合。两者都使对方获得新生，正如学生、教师和艺术家们的创造性合作互相激活一样。

上图：花园剧场，新活动中心的出口以及北部的庭院连接着附近的小道

above: the Garden Theater and new entry activate the north courtyard and connect to adjacent paths

DONG-HWA
NATIONAL
UNIVERSITY

东华国立大学

A fertile valley between the coastal and central mountains of Taiwan is the site for a new university campus. Eight undergraduate and graduate schools—including engineering, arts, and sciences—will accommodate more than one thousand faculty, five hundred staff, and ten thousand students. Moore Ruble Yudell's master plan juxtaposes an axis—oriented to the mountains—against a meandering water park of connected ponds and lakes. Inspired by river deltas near the site, the water park activates and complements the formal geometries of the plan and recalls the classic use of water to delineate the boundaries of palaces and temple complexes throughout Asia.

In the central campus, the library, administration, and other pan-university uses occupy sites along the main axis flanked by courtyard complexes that house individual schools. The courtyards provide an outdoor social heart for each school, and also serve to shelter trees from frequent typhoons. Faculty and student housing, theaters, and sports and community facilities are sited along the water, which widens to mark special places—the central plaza, the student union—and doubles as a key element in the system of campus flood control.

Moore Ruble Yudell's work as master planners has focused on design of the overall campus infrastructure, public space, and landscape, with extensive design and color guidelines to establish a context for individual buildings. Influences of culture and climate are expressed in broad, tree-shaded boulevards and playfully spirited bridges, which celebrate the daily movements of students as they bicycle to and from residences and classes.

在台湾岛的海岸与中央山脉之间的一条肥沃山谷中，有一个新大学校园的地段。八个本科生和研究生学院——包括工程、艺术和科学——将容纳千余名教师、500名职工以及一万名学生。MRY的总体规划将一条朝向山脉的轴线与一个蜿蜒的由相连的池塘和湖泊组成的水公园并置在一起。受地段附近的三角洲启发，水公园激活了平面的几何形式，并对它进行了补充，使人想起亚洲经典的水体用法——形成宫殿和寺庙群的边界。

在校园中央，图书馆、行政区域以及其他全校性功能区域占据了主轴线两侧的地段，主轴线旁边同时还排布着每个学院的庭院组团。这些庭院为每个学院提供了室外社交中心，同时使树木免受频繁台风的毁坏。教师和学生的住宿、剧院、体育和社区设施等沿水边布置，其间的延宽处安置着一些特殊场所——如中央广场、学生活动大楼——他们同时也在校园洪水控制系统中起到重要作用。

MRY的总体规划工作聚焦于整个校园的基础设施、公共空间以及景观的设计，同时，制定了设计和色彩的大体方针，为单体建筑确立起文脉背景。文化和气候的影响在宽阔的林荫大道和有趣的小桥中得以体现，它们展示了学生们每日的运动：在住宅与教室间来回骑行。

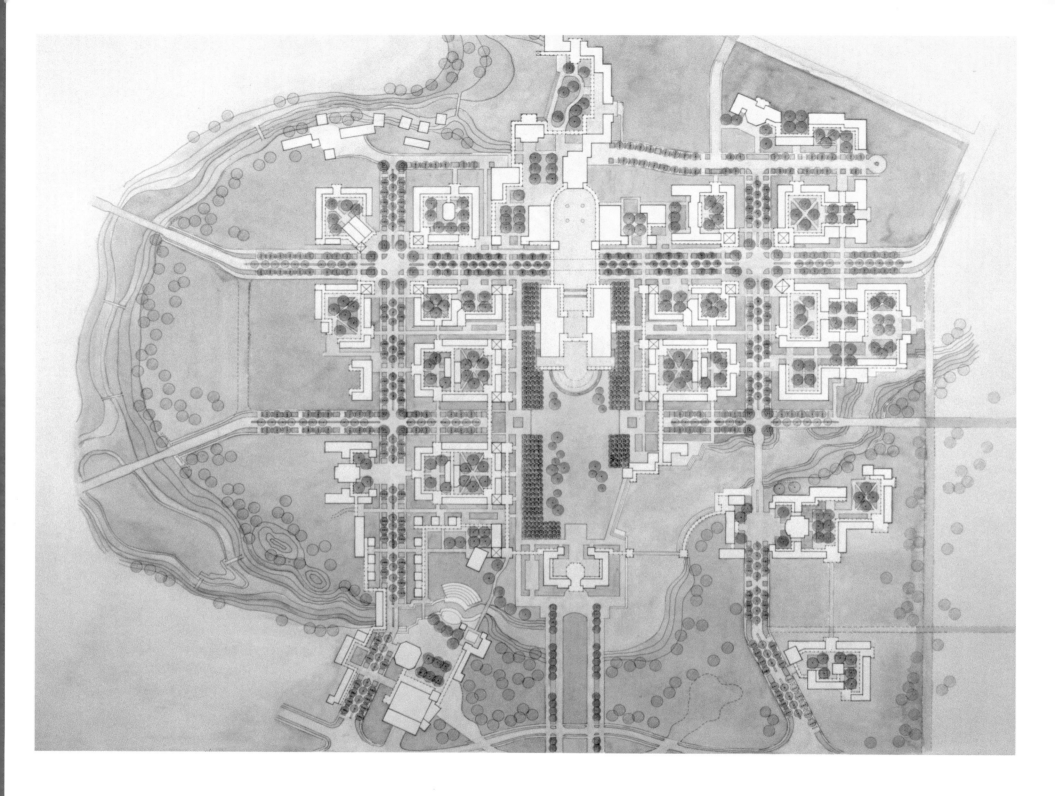

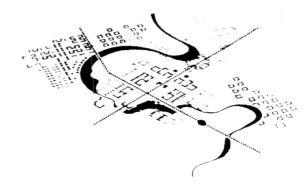

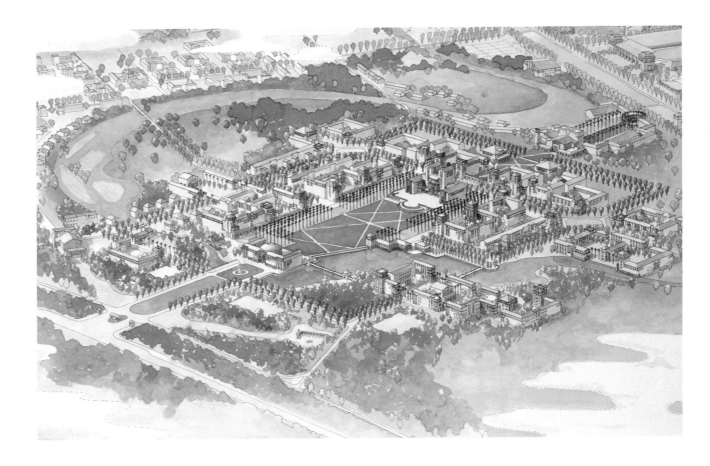

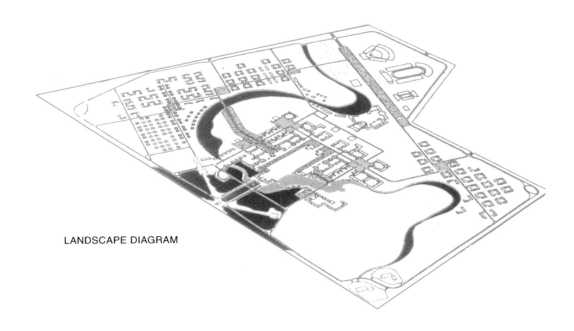

LANDSCAPE DIAGRAM

BUILDING UP

PLACE AND HABITATION AT HIGHER DENSITIES

建造　更高密度区的场所和居住

人口的增长和对资源的更新利用的需求都暗示了城市密度不可避免的增长。更高的密度减少了蔓延，增加了人性互动。但是高密度所面临的挑战是要保持住场所感、人性的尺度、个体的尊严以及社区的凝聚力。我们相信，即使是最大的城市，也可以通过建造提供在多种社会尺度上的有意义的体验并保持与自然环境之间的联系。营造出的场所，使我们在其中的生活具有尊严、与自然相和谐并融于社区，这是当代建筑学所面临的最重要的挑战之一。

The growth of population and the need to renew our resources both suggest that greater urban density is inevitable. Such density can minimize sprawl and increase human interaction. But the challenge of greater density is to preserve a sense of place, a humane scale, the dignity of the individual, and the coherence of the community. We believe that even the largest cities can be built to provide meaningful experiences at many social scales and to preserve a connection to the natural environment. Creating places where we can live with dignity, in harmony with nature, and supported by our community is among the most important challenges of contemporary architecture.

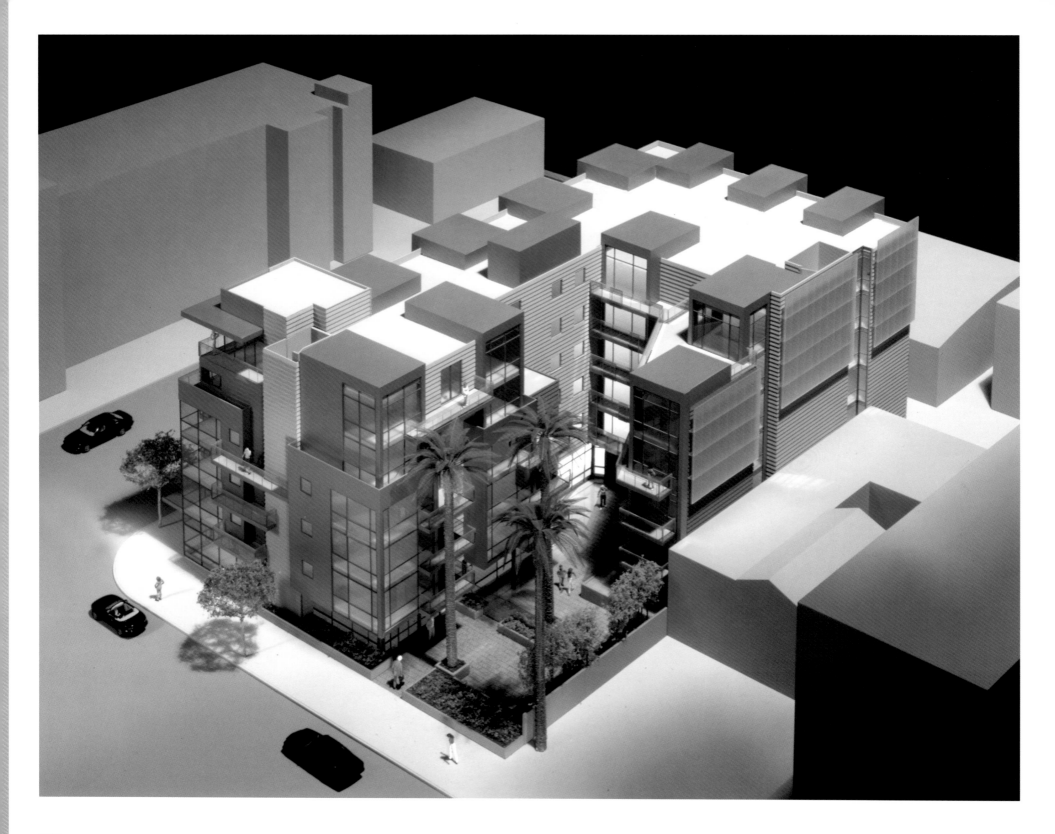

606 BROADWAY

SANTA MONICA, CALIFORNIA, USA
圣莫尼卡，加利福尼亚州，美国

606百老汇大街住宅

OPEN DENSITY: CREATING A NEIGHBORHOOD IN AN URBAN ENVIRONMENT

606 Broadway is a six-story mixed-use infill development with rental housing and three levels of below-grade parking. The building site is located on the southeast corner of Broadway and Sixth Street in downtown Santa Monica. The project has been designed to respond to the different characteristics of the two intersecting streets, reflecting and reinforcing their identity within the urban density.

Broadway, on the north side of the project, has a strong urban quality. The building edge along this street is retail-oriented along the ground floor, supporting pedestrian activity and a city sensibility. On the other hand, Sixth Street on the west side of the building has a more residential quality, with apartment buildings lining both sides of the street. The residential side of the building sets back from the street with a sense of privacy and well-being.

On both sides of the building, the upper floors are articulated by a syncopated rhythm of balconies and glassy bays that optimize the view corridors toward the Santa Monica Mountains to the north and the ocean to the west. The public entrance at the corner of Broadway and Sixth Street is anchored by a colorful tower element and animated by a café on the ground floor. Café tables spill out into an inviting garden court, providing an active street presence.

A material palette of alternating zinc panels, "Hardie Board" concrete panels, and glazing modulates the façade of the building. Glaze coating in different levels of translucency and opacity, and fretted glass screens reinforce this patterning. Photovoltaic panels on the southwest elevation and roof provide an additional energy source for the building and meet the city's sustainability guidelines.

The residential lobby is approached through a series of courtyards. Residents enter through the public café court, with its lush grove of trees, before reaching a second, more private garden that provides access to the building. Amenities are oriented toward the garden court, and provide opportunities to foster community among the residents. At the end of the garden is the secured entrance to the recreation room. The units range in size from 700 to 1,000 square feet, with some two-story loft apartments. A percentage of the units are designated as affordable housing as required by the city of Santa Monica. The light-filled units have large private balconies that create an open, positive feel to the homes, welcoming the ocean breezes into the apartments.

The landscape design concept for the project is defined by the different characteristics of the two streets on the north and west sides of the project. Dramatic masses of drought-tolerant shrubs in the Sixth Street garden court emphasize the residential quality on this edge of the project. The courtyard's large Canary Island Palms connect to the borrowed landscape of the neighborhood. A re-circulating water feature at the base of a planter reflects the patterns of water currents and shadows from a line of Black Bamboo onto the courtyard walls.

开放的密度：在城市环境中营造邻里街区

606百老汇大街住宅是一个具有混合功能的开发项目，有6层出租住宅及地下3层停车场。建筑地段位于圣莫尼卡市区百老汇大街与第六大街交叉口的东南角。方案设计要对这两条相交大街的不同特征作出回应，在城市密度下反映并加强它们的个性。

项目北边的百老汇大街，有一种很强烈的城市性。这条大街两侧的建筑界面在一层都用于底商，支持行人的活动和城市的敏感性。而另一边，建筑西侧第六大街的性质则更偏于居住，大街两侧都排列着公寓楼。建筑的住宅部分由街边向后退让，形成一定的隐私感和安全性。

建筑两边的上层都展现出阳台和玻璃隔间的切分节奏，优化了朝向北边圣莫尼卡山脉和西边海洋的视觉廊道。在两条街道的街角，公共入口的位置被一个彩色的塔形元素固定，并由一个一层的咖啡馆带来活力。咖啡馆的桌子散布在一个引人入胜的花园庭院中，提供了一个有活力的街景。

一组由交互式锌板、"硬片"混凝土面板和玻璃板组成的材料配置调节着建筑的立面。玻璃板笼罩在不同程度的透明度和蒙胧之中，装饰性的玻璃幕墙加强了立面的图案感。西南立面上和屋顶上的光电板为建筑提供了额外的能源，并且符合了城市的可持续性方针。

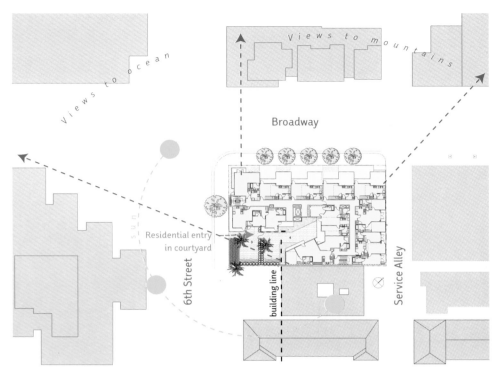

住宅大厅可从一系列庭院到达。居民们从公共咖啡馆庭院进入，之中种有青葱的小树，然后到达第二个更私密的花园，由此进入建筑。各种便利设施面向花园庭院，提供了在居民中培养市区的机会。在花园尽端，有一个通向娱乐室的安全入口。单元面积从65到93平方米不等，有些是阁楼跃层。出于圣莫尼卡市的要求，一部分单元被设定为"可支付住宅"。光线充足的单元有私密的大阳台，将海风引入家中，为"家"营造了一种开放、积极的感觉。

这个项目的景观设计概念是由建筑北侧和西侧的两条道路的不同性质决定的。在第六大街花园庭院中戏剧性地种有丛丛耐旱灌木，强调了该项目这一边界上的住宅性质。庭院中的高大加那利群岛棕榈与从附近"借来"的景色相融。在一个花架底部的一个循环水装置倒映出水流的图案，以及一行墨竹在庭院墙上的投影。

The residential courtyard is animated by an art installation, consisting of an array of aluminum "bamboo" poles with arching light rods, which spans one entire façade of balconies and announces the entry to the building. Intended as a welcoming gesture to residents, but also prominently visible from the café and public court, this art installation is inspired by the colors and forms found in natural bamboo. The colored tubes have random spacing and lengths to convey the serene, screen-like presence of bamboo. Their vivid colors have been carefully selected to evoke young and old stalks.

这个居住性庭院由一个艺术装置激活，这个艺术装置由一列铝制"竹"杆和弯成弓形的发光棒组成，跨越了整个阳台的立面，并标示出建筑的入口。这个艺术装置被设想为用来迎接居民，但同时也能从咖啡馆和公共庭院中明显地看到，它的灵感来自于自然竹子中找到的色彩与形式。彩杆的间距和长度是随机的，表达出竹子宁静的屏风般的外观。它们的活泼色彩是经过细心选择的，用以表明新茎和老茎。

FAVORVIEW PALACE
EAST DISTRICT

汇景新城东区

HARMONY WITH NATURE

The defining framework of this master plan features an engaging interplay of the site's existing natural features with residential buildings and an expansive Central Green Area to create lively pedestrian-centered neighborhoods. A major goal is to preserve the site's outstanding natural topographical features to the South by enhancing the lush landscaping on the hills and providing pedestrian paths to panoramic lookout pavilions. The design also envisions the Urban Spine, a strong East-West open space that connects to the existing Central District with a new pedestrian overpass over Huijingdong Road.

The careful shaping of spaces, paths of movement, qualities of entry and identity will work together to encourage creative interaction among residents. A cohesive system of walkable streets and paths will engender a comfortable and habitable place that fosters a sense of community.

THE CENTRAL GREEN AREA

A Central Green Area will serve as the social and recreational heart of the District, providing a scenic series of outdoor spaces and water features through the central part of the site, extending from the existing Southern hills to the residential high-rises along Keyun Road to the north. Accessed by pedestrian paths and animated with rich landscaping, bridges, and pavilions, this Central Green Area intersects with the Urban Spine to form the District's major natural feature, offering a multi-layered amenity with diverse opportunities for leisure and recreation activities.

INTEGRATING BUILDINGS WITH LANDSCAPE

The master plan designates a series of themed neighborhoods, each with its own identity, parks, and open spaces. All residential buildings are oriented to the open space network, providing a coherent visual and physical connection to the Central Green Area. The massing of the buildings steps from lower bar buildings along the Central Green Area to the high-rise towers at the outer peripheries of the site.

The bar buildings and towers are treated with varying colors to provide identity and character. The bases have stone banding on two to four floors, the façades lightening as they rise up toward the sky, and the upper floors are treated with colored plaster walls. Bay windows and regular windows provide variety to the elevations, while lanterns add a sense of dynamic movement to the roofscape of the buildings. Special elements such as glass canopies at building entrances provide a sense of additional identity and variety. The hot and humid tropical climate of Guangzhou makes the use of sun-shading features a critical necessity for all buildings. These devices can include both vertical (sliding screens, louvers and shutters) or horizontal elements (trellises, canopies and overhangs).

与自然和谐相处

这个总体规划的决定性框架的特点是：地段原有的自然特征与住宅楼和一个广阔的绿色区域之间进行吸引人的互动，创造了以行人为中心的活力街区。一个主要的目标是保留地段南侧突出的自然地形特征，于是我们改善了山坡上的丰富景观，并提供了通往观景亭台的行人道路。我们在设计中还构想了"城市脊骨"，这是一个强烈的东西向的开放空间，它通过汇景东路上的一架新人行天桥与原有的中心区相连。

空间的细心塑造、运动的路径、入口的性质以及个性特征等将共同作用，鼓励居民间的创造性互动。一个由可步行街道和道路组成的连贯系统将营造一个舒适且适于居住的空间，有助于形成社区感。

中央绿色区

一个中央绿色区将成为该地区的社交和休闲中心，在地段的中心部分将有一系列风景优美的室外空间和水域景观，这个区域从原有的南侧山坡延伸到北侧可云路旁的高层住宅楼。中央绿色区与行人道相连，丰富的景观、桥梁和亭台等为它带来活力，它与"城市脊骨"相交，形成了区域内主要的自然特征，提供了多层次的便捷设施以及多样的休闲、娱乐活动机会。

建筑与景观的整合

总体规划中分配了一系列的主题街区，每个都有其独特的特征、公园和开放空间。所有的住宅楼都朝向公共空间网络，与中央绿色区建立起连贯的视觉和实质联系。建筑的密度从中央绿色区两侧的低层条形建筑到地段外围的高层塔楼逐渐增高。

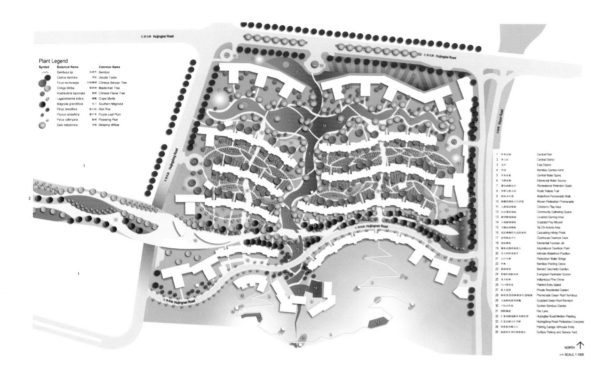

Plant Legend

Symbol	Botanical Name		Common Name
	Bambusa sp		Bamboo
	Cedrus deodara		Deodar Cedar
	Ficus microcarpa		Chinese Banyan Tree
	Ginkgo biloba		Maidenhair Tree
	Koelreuteria bipinnata		Chinese Flame Tree
	Lagerstroemia indica		Crape Myrtle
	Magnolia grandiflora		Southern Magnolia
	Pinus densiflora		Red Pine
	Prunus cerasifera		Purple Leaf Plum
	Pyrus calleryana		Flowering Pear
	Salix babylonica		Weeping Willow

1 Central Park
2 Central District
3 East District
4 Bamboo Garden Axis
5 Central Water Spine
6 Elemental Water Source
7 Recreational Retention Basin
8 Rustic Nature Trail
9 Waterfront Promenade Walk
10 Woven Pedestrian Promenade
11 Children's Play Area
12 Community Gathering Space
13 Covered Gaming Area
14 Sculpted Play Mound
15 Tai Chi Activity Area
16 Cascading Infinity Pools
17 Clubhouse Overlook Deck
18 Elemental Fountain Jet
19 Inspirational Overlook Point
20 Intimate Waterfront Pavilion
21 Pedestrian Water Bridge
22 Bamboo Planting Grove
23 Banded Geometry Garden
24 Evergreen Perimeter Screen
25 Indigenous Pine Grove
26 Planted Entry Island
27 Private Residential Garden
28 Promenade Green Roof Terminus
29 Sculpted Garden Roof Element
30 Sunken Bamboo Garden
31 Fire Lane
32 Hujingbei Road Median Planting
33 Hujingbei Road Pedestrian Overpass
34 Parking Garage Vehicular Entry
35 Surface Parking and Service Yard

NORTH ↑

SCALE 1:1000

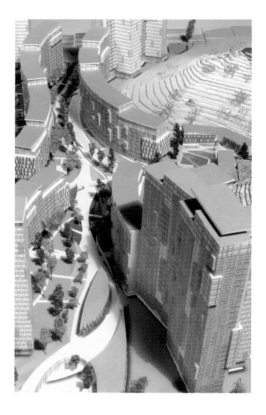

180

RESIDENTIAL GARDENS WITH DISTINCT CHARACTERS
A network of neighborhood-scaled gardens and court-yards provides welcome open space for residential buildings on individual blocks. Together they create a series of "fingers" or "bands" of more intimate open spaces that connect to the Central Green Area. These open spaces are designed to focus pedestrian activity within and around nearby buildings, encouraging inter-action and creating an attractive image for residential life. A specific landscape theme is proposed for each garden to establish character for each neighborhood and add to the rich architectural qualities of the overall District.

条形建筑被赋予不同颜色，以形成个性特征。在2~4层的底座上有条石带，立面接近天空时变得更加轻盈，在上层则用彩色抹灰墙面。凸窗和普通窗为立面带来多样性，而天窗则为建筑的屋顶景观增加了一种动态感。特殊的元素，比如建筑入口处的玻璃雨棚，额外增加了特征感和多样性。广州湿热的热带气候让遮阳构件变成所有建筑的重要必需品。这些构件既包括竖向的(如可滑动的屏风、条形百叶等)也包括横向的(如格架、天棚和悬吊物)。

独具特色的住宅花园
在单个街区中，一个由街区尺度的花园和庭院组成的网络成为受居民欢迎的开放空间。把它们合起来，则形成了一系列与中央绿色区相连的的更为亲和的"指形"或"带形"开放空间。这些开放空间旨在把行人活动聚焦在附近的建筑内部或周围，鼓励互动，并创造了一个吸引人的居民生活景象。每个花园有一个特定的景观主题，为每个街区确立了性格特征，并为整个区域增加了丰富的建筑品质。

NEI-HU RESIDENTIAL TOWERS

内湖住宅塔楼

This high-end residential project is located in the Nei-Hu District, a newly developed district about seven miles to the east of downtown Taipei. The roughly triangular site covers 6,400 square meters and faces a major tree-lined boulevard directly across from the future American Institute in Taipei project, also in design by Moore Ruble Yudell. The project comprises 136 units of housing along with public amenities, for a total building area of 48,000 square meters.

Our design is based on a configuration of two residential towers engaged with a sequence of gardens at the base. The challenge was to create an elegant architectural expression while incorporating a set of pre-determined floor plans prepared by our associate architects in Taipei. These floor plans stipulated substantial programmatic, zoning, structural, and service requirements, including heavy concrete columns and beams around the perimeter of the towers.

GARDENS AND FOUNTAINS
A sequence of public plazas, serene gardens and water features engages the plinth at the base of the towers to provide welcome shade and cool fountains in the hot, humid climate. The gardens are a narrative to be experienced either individually, or as a continuous journey. The edges of the plinth are enlivened with shady arcades while its stone walls are sculpted with stepped planters to transition down to the street and sidewalk level.

STEPPED TOWERS
In massing, the two towers gradually step up along the boulevard, offering a richly articulated elevation to pe-destrians and motorists. The north tower contains three units on each floor, and increases in height from 16 to 20 floors. The taller, larger south tower provides four units on each floor while ranging from 22 to 26 floors. Each residential unit has separate elevator access as well as a garden entry. Windows and larger groups of glazed bays are carefully placed to relate to major rooms and offer expansive views to the forests and lake toward the east and south. Our strategy aims to achieve a fresh, contemporary character while preserving a Classical elegance and order.

The base and lower floors of the towers are strengthened with prominent stone walls that anchor the buildings to the ground and enhance the sense of formal presence. Some walls are splayed to accommodate the structural columns and beams, creating angled, recessed pockets of windows and balconies that lend a varied play of shadows on the elevations.

The middle portion of the building is animated by an interplay of prefabricated concrete panels with shifting windows that correlate to the structural and view requirements from the units. The ribbed stone texture on the buff-colored concrete panels catch the light and enhance the rich quality of the façades.

The large, syncopated glass bays establish another layer of movement on the building exteriors. Alternating rows of flush, buff-colored rows and white projecting bands mark the floor levels, while imparting calm and continuity to the façade.

这个高端住宅项目坐落于内湖区，一个台北市东距市中心约11.27公里的新开发区。这个近似于三角形的地段占据了6,400平方米，紧靠一条种有行道树的主要大道，大道正对面就是将要建造的台北美国协会（American Institute in Taipei，同样由MRY设计）的地段。这个项目由136个住宅单元组成，同时具备公共便利设施，建筑面积达48,000平方米。

我们要设计两幢住宅塔楼的外观以及它们底层的一系列花园。面临的挑战是，既要创造一个优美的建筑形式，又要将一系列由我们的台北合伙设计人预先设计好的楼层平面合并进来。这些楼层平面里制定好了实质的计划、分区、结构和服务要求，包括塔楼外围的重混凝土柱梁。

花园和喷泉
一系列的公共广场、宁静的花园和水景与塔楼的底座一起，在湿热的气候中提供了受欢迎的阴影和凉爽的喷泉。叙事性的花园既可以单独地被体验，也可以作为一个连贯的旅程来欣赏。遮荫的拱廊为建筑底座的边缘带来活力，底座的石墙与梯级式花台塑造在一起，向下过渡到街道和人行道平面。

梯级式的塔楼
在密度上，两幢塔楼沿着街道逐渐增大，为行人和司机提供了一个设计丰富的立面。北边的塔楼每层容纳3个单元，在16-20层中有更多。南边更高更大的塔楼在22层到26层之间每层容纳4个单元。每个住宅单元都有单独的电梯到达，并有一个花园入口。窗户和大组的玻璃隔间被仔细地布置，并和主要的房间联系起来，提供了朝向东边和南边森林与湖泊的广阔景致。我们的目标是在保留经典的优雅和秩序的同时，创造一种新鲜的、现代的特征。

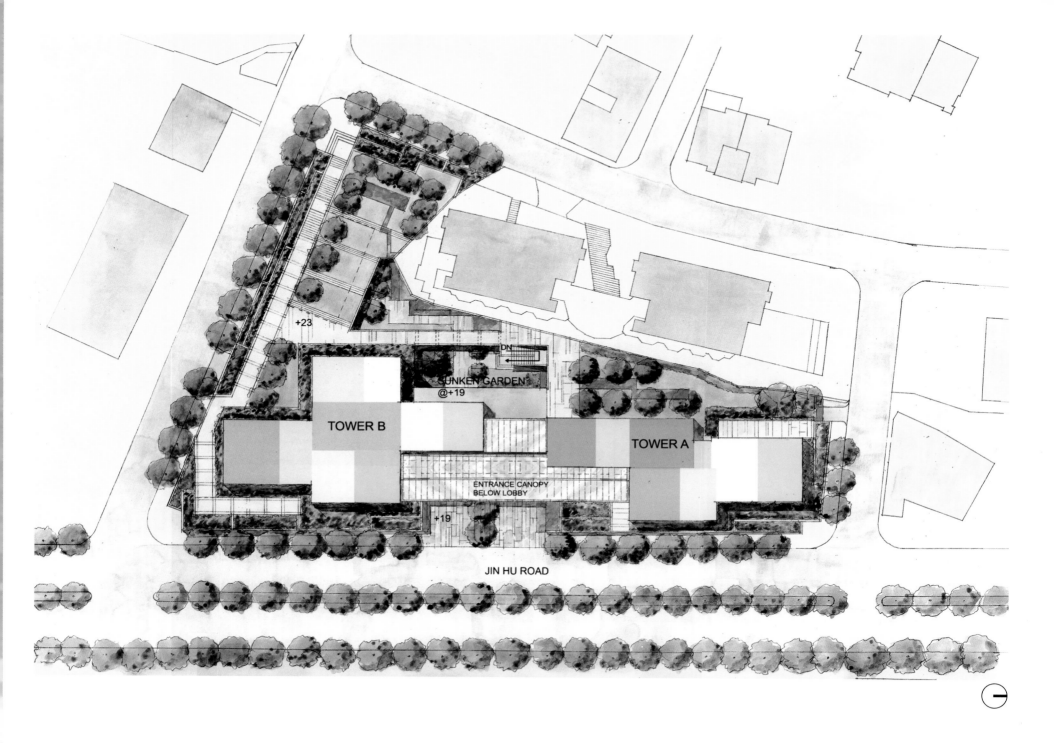

TOWER B

TOWER A

SUNKEN GARDEN
@+19

+23

DN

ENTRANCE CANOPY
BELOW LOBBY

+19

JIN HU ROAD

above: roof plan

上图：屋顶平面

The stepped massing of the upper floors relate to the scale of the city while providing a varied, interesting silhouette. The tower tops have the lightest character, with their large glass bays acting as "lanterns." The overall glazing system is a contemporary expression of the Arts & Crafts manner with an elegant pattern of frames and mullions.

塔楼的底座和较低的几层由突出的石墙加强，石墙把建筑固定在地面上，同时增加了外观的正式感。一些墙面向外倾斜，包围住了结构柱梁，形成倾斜的内凹窗洞和阳台，增加了立面上阴影的多样性。

预制混凝土板和变换的窗户——这是由单元的结构和景观要求决定的——为建筑的中部带来活力。浅黄色混凝土板上的肋状石材形成光影，提高了立面的丰富性。

具有切分节奏的大型玻璃隔间形成了建筑立面上的另外一层韵律。交替的红色和浅黄色横条与白色的突出带标志出楼层平面，同时传达出立面的平静感与连续性。

较高的几层梯级式的外观与城市的尺度相协调，并提供了一个多样化的有趣轮廓。塔楼的顶端最为轻盈，上面的大玻璃隔间形成灯笼般的天窗。整体的玻璃装配系统是工艺美术风格的一种现代表达，具有优雅的窗框和窗棂图案。

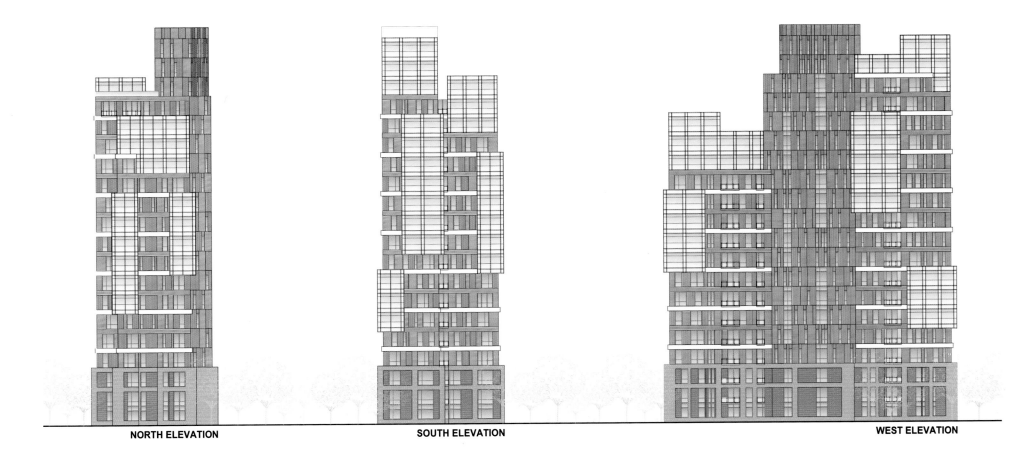

NORTH ELEVATION　　　　**SOUTH ELEVATION**　　　　**WEST ELEVATION**

above: North Tower A Elevations　　　　上图：北塔立面

11th FLOOR PLAN @ + 61.70

Scale 1:200

16th FLOOR PLAN @ + 79.20

Scale 1:200

6th FLOOR PLAN @ + 44.20

Scale 1:200

2nd FLOOR PLAN @ + 26.70

Scale 1:200

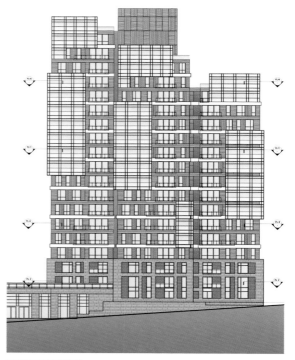

EAST ELEVATION

WATERMARK TOWER

SAN FRANCISCO, CALIFORNIA, USA
旧金山，加利福尼亚州，美国

WATERMARK塔楼

The Watermark residential tower commands an auspicious site on San Francisco's Embarcadero waterfront, right alongside the Bay Bridge. It is Moore Ruble Yudell's second high-rise condominium project for Lend Lease Development, following the Regatta Wharf Housing at Jackson's Landing in Sydney, Australia.

From master planning and programming through Design Development, Moore Ruble Yudell worked closely with Lend Lease's marketing and management staff, as well as San Francisco city planners and waterfront design review groups.

The design considers the site's spectacular setting on the San Francisco Bay, at the confluence of varying urban districts and their respective scales: high-rise office buildings to the north toward downtown, three to four story townhouse scale with several towers in the South Beach vicinity, and the colossal scale of the nearby Bay Bridge.

The building's tower form is articulated with step-backs, or "shoulders," which along with projecting bays and balconies, enhance the verticality of the building, while affording maximum view opportunities for all apartments. The step-backs also facilitate optimum response to program in accommodating the mix of one- two- and three-bedroom and penthouse units.

Soil conditions dictated that parking be accommodated above ground in a three-story podium structure. This building base is shaped to relate to the scale of surrounding three- and four-story apartment buildings, and its expression is carefully integrated with the tower as well as the surrounding context. A number of "loft" units in the base address the street, to avoid a "parking garage" expression. The light, transparent expression of the tower, with its glass balcony balustrades and light-colored spandrels of glass and metal, is brought down into the base at the monumental Bryant/Beale corner, while cast-stone walls punctuated with recessed entries, windows and openings articulate the base walls.

坐落在海湾桥边上的Watermark塔楼公寓占据着旧金山内河码头滨水区中的一个有利地段。这是MRY继澳大利亚悉尼杰克逊口岸的赛艇码头住宅后，为租借开发公司设计的第二个高层私有公寓楼。

从总体规划和计划开始，贯穿整个设计开发，MRY与租借开发公司的营销和管理人员以及旧金山的城市规划者还有滨水设计评价团进行了密切的合作。

设计考虑到了地段位于旧金山湾的壮丽景致以及汇集于此的多种城市街区和它们各自的规模和尺度：北边朝向市区的高层办公楼；南部海滩周围的3~4层联排住宅与几座塔楼以及附近巨大的海湾桥。

建筑的塔楼形式中精心设计了向后的退进，或者称之为建筑的"肩"，它们与向外突出的隔间和阳台一起，提高了建筑的垂直性，并为所有公寓单元都提供了最大的观景机会。向后的退进同时还回应了项目的需求：容纳多种住宅的混合，包括带有1个、2个或3个卧室的公寓，以及屋顶的高级单元。

土壤性质决定了停车场要放在地上的一个3层高的底座结构中。建筑底座的塑造与周围三、四层的公寓楼的尺度相关联，它的表达与高塔以及周围环境精心地融合在一起。底部有一些"阁楼"状的单元，朝向街道，以避免一种"停车场"式的外观。塔楼有玻璃的阳台栏杆和浅色的玻璃和金属拱肩，呈现出轻盈、透明的外观，它一直延续到底部著名的Bryant/Beale街角处，在这里，人造石墙上点缀着内凹的入口，窗户与洞口使底座墙面连成一体。

REGATTA WHARF HOUSING AT JACKSON'S LANDING

杰克逊口岸的赛艇码头住宅

Sydney, far and away one of the world's most delightful residential cities, owes its grandeur and charm to the harbor: a rich shoreline geography of alternating headlands and coves. Around each cove a beautifully scaled neighborhood tumbles down a lushly landscaped hillside to a small beach, where an elegant local restaurant has taken over an old pavilion next to the park. Around Circular Quay, at one of the larger coves, Sydney gathers its renowned collection of landmarks: the Opera House, Sydney Harbour Bridge, and the rugged, historic neighborhood known as The Rocks.

Further in along the waterfront, past the splashy tourist attractions of Darling Harbor, is the older industrial district of Pyrmont, where an enormous sugar mill site has been re-planned as a high-end residential development—"Jackson's Landing."

BELVEDERE

As a foreground to the project, occupying the choicest cut of its real estate, Regatta Wharf has been shaped according to the prime directive of Sydney housing development: capture the view. We sought to heighten the experience of living at the water's edge in Sydney's mild climate by providing each unit in the 250-unit complex with not just a balcony, but a generous veranda—a real outdoor room. The verandas are a high-rise interpretation of the classic Australian porch, complete with power and gas for the barbeque. The verandas are stacked at corners or wrap around living rooms, giving an inside-outside laciness to the large mass of the towers.

RUGGED REFINEMENT

The towers cluster around two courts, one centered on a circular mound and fountain, and the other offering a narrow stepped garden from the street down to the waterfront promenade. Between the two tower groups a small park looks out to the harbor and back to the great stone bluff, through which a dramatic stairway has been chiseled.

The massive, cut rock walls behind Regatta Wharf, and the industrial heritage of the site's context inspired spare, solid walls with punched windows on façades facing the bluff, in complete contrast to the louver-and-glass openness of the waterfront elevations. These opposing aspects mirror our own outsider's view of two keynotes of Australian culture—the tautly pragmatic realism and the studied appreciation of the finer things in life.

悉尼，世界上最适宜居住的城市之一，其伟大与魅力应归功于它的海港：一条陆海交错的丰富海岸线。在每个小海湾周围，依附着一片尺度优美、景观繁茂的山坡，由上至下延伸到一片小海滩上，在公园旁的一幢老亭子里，有一家雅致的当地餐厅。在环形码头周围，最大的几个小湾之一处聚集着悉尼最著名的地标：歌剧院、海港大桥，还有那高低不平的历史街区——岩石区。

沿着海岸线继续前行，经过受到旅游者盛誉的达令港，则来到了较古老的Pyrmont工业区，在这里，一个巨大的糖工厂地段被重新规划为一个高端住宅开发项目——"杰克逊口岸"。

观景楼

作为这个开发项目的前景，赛艇码头占据了土地中最上乘的一块地段，它的规划遵从了悉尼住宅开发的首要原则：获取景致。我们希望，在温和的气候中，悉尼水边的居住体验可以得到提高，于是我们为每个单元（这是综合体的250个单元之一）提供的不仅是一个阳台，而是一个宽阔的凉台——一间真正的室外房间。这种凉台是古典式的澳大利亚门廊的一种高层演绎，它完整到还拥有用于烧烤的电气。这些凉台位于转角处，或是包围着起居室，在塔楼的高大体量中形成一种内－外花边感。

above: for residential life in Sydney, the view is everything   上图：住在悉尼，面面观   **197**

粗犷与精致并存

塔楼围绕着两个庭院形成组团，其中一个以一座圆台和喷泉为中心，而另一个则提供了一个狭窄的台地花园，可以从街道向下通到滨水步道。在这两个塔楼组团之间，一个小公园可以望向海港，而向后则可以看到巨大的石崖，石崖中凿刻着一条戏剧性的楼梯。

赛艇码头后面巨大的、经过雕刻的岩石墙以及地段环境遗留下的的工业遗产，为我们带来了灵感，形成立面上打有窗洞的简朴而坚固的墙面，它面对着石崖，与滨水方向由天窗和玻璃形成的开放性立面形成了强烈对比。这两个对立面也反映了我们作为外乡人对澳大利亚文化的两个重要方面的看法——简洁的、实用的现实主义，以及对生活中美好事物的精心赞赏。

FAIRMONT HOTEL ADDITION

FAIRMONT酒店扩建

The addition to the luxury Fairmont Hotel in San Jose provides multiple connections, both visual axes and lines of movement, to link the new building with its surrounding district in the center of San Jose's elegant downtown. The special qualities of the site and the streets around it are brought into and through the planning of the addition, capturing the energy of this vibrant urban space. The curved form of the new building creates a gateway to the western entrance to the pedestrian mall, El Paseo de San Antonio. At street level, this gateway quality provides a welcoming gesture, a place of gathering and arrival for the neighborhood as well as the Hotel itself.

The addition's strong form responds to two adjacent major spaces. The East-West Paseo marches along the North façade of the building, between the addition and the existing hotel. To the West of the building is downtown San Jose's main green space, the expansive Cesar Chavez Plaza Park, bordered by Market Street

The building is shaped to achieve two urban design goals—to pull the Park into the Paseo, and to extend the Paseo out into the Park. As a result, the building form becomes both perpendicular and parallel to Cesar Chavez Plaza Park.

Toward the West side, the addition is inflected with a sweeping curve that forms a gateway for the Paseo. The curve allows the western end of the building to become parallel to the Park. Toward the East side of the project, the building mass is perpendicular to the Park. Here, it is parallel to the existing hotel and presents the southern edge to the Paseo, containing retail spaces and restaurants at the base that connect this part with the continuation of the Paseo across First Street to the East. As one moves West, the curving shape of the addition opens the Paseo to provide views of the Park and the Tech Museum of Innovation, as well as a visual link to Park Boulevard on the other side of Cesar Chavez Plaza Park.

The new building itself consists of a traditional division into base, middle and top. These three vertical components relate to both the surrounding urban context and the existing grand hotel. The addition is not a static building, there is a sense of continuous movement offered by the curve, one's perspective is always changing along the façade of the building. This sense of movement is reinforced by the horizontal bands of colored pre-cast concrete on the façade.

The base is clad in richly textured limestone and precast panels, providing a strong urban connection to the Paseo. Restaurants and retail spaces within the base animate the Paseo and provide a link between the Park and the rest of the Paseo further East. The second level holds meeting rooms doubling as banquet rooms, along with prefunction space. A bridge on the second level crosses the Paseo, linking the new meeting rooms to those in the existing hotel. It is made of glass with a light steel structure.

对圣何塞的Fairmont豪华酒店的加建提供了多种连接，包括视觉轴线和运动路线，它们把新建筑与其周围区域——圣何塞优美的市中心联系起来。我们感受到这个有活力的城市空间的能量，于是将地段及其周边街道的特殊性质带入到加建规划中，并贯穿其过程。新建筑的曲线形式营造了一个通向El Paseo de San Antonio步行商业街西入口的通道。在街道平面上，这个通道展示了一个欢迎的姿态，成为一个周围的街区以及酒店自身的聚集和到达的场所。

加建建筑的强烈形式回应了附近的两个主要空间。东西向的Paseo从建筑的北立面前通过，夹在加建部分和原有酒店之间。建筑的西边是圣何塞市中心的主要绿化空间——以市场街为界的广阔的Cesar Chavez广场公园。

建筑的形态塑造是为了达到两个城市设计目标——将公园引入到Paseo中，以及将Paseo延伸到公园里。于是，建筑成为一个与凯萨·查维斯广场公园既垂直又平行的形式。

在西侧，加建部分进行弯曲，成为一条弧度很大的曲线，形成了通向Paseo的通道。这条曲线使建筑的西端与公园平行。在项目的东侧，建筑体块则与公园垂直。在这里，它与原有酒店平行，成为Paseo的南边界。底层包含的零售空间以及餐厅，将该部分与穿过第一大街延伸到东边的连贯的Paseo连接起来。人向西移动的时候，加建部分的曲线形状使Paseo敞开，人可以看到公园的景致以及创新技术博物馆，还可以形成与凯萨·查维斯广场公园另一侧公园大道之间的视觉联系。

新建筑本身按传统分割分为底座、中部和顶部。这三个垂直的组成部分不仅与周围的城市环境相关，也与原有的大酒店相关。加建部分不是一幢静态的建筑，而是由曲线形成了一种连续的运动感，使人的视角沿着建筑立面一直在改变。这种运动感由立面上的现浇混凝土水平彩色带加强。

The middle and largest component contains guest rooms and is most directly related to the existing hotel. Its understated, quieter character serves to contrast with the prominent base and dynamic top. A graceful pattern of window openings and vertical/horizontal bands of glass-fiber reinforced concrete in two aggregate finishes create a simple yet vibrant movement on the curving facade.

Also containing guest rooms, the top three floors respond to the skyline of downtown and provide a light and transparent flourish to the building. The zinc pitched roof acts with high windows and tall zinc columns to form a landmark lantern that glows at night.

底座覆有材质丰富的石灰石和预制板，提供了与Paseo之间强烈的城市性连接。底座中的餐厅和零售空间为Paseo带来活力，并在公园与Paseo东部之间建立了联系。2层容纳了双倍会议室形成的宴会厅及其前厅。2层的一架由玻璃和轻钢结构建成的桥横跨过Paseo，将新、老建筑的会议室连接起来。

中部是最大的组成部分，包含了客房，并与原有酒店有着最直接的关系。它较为简朴、安静的特征与向外突出的底座和充满动感的顶部形成对比。优雅的开窗模式和两端垂直/水平方向的玻璃纤维钢筋混凝土带共同创造了曲线立面上的一种简单而有活力的运动感。

顶部三层同样包含了客房，回应了市中心的天际线，赋予建筑一种轻盈、透明的姿态。锌板坡屋顶与高窗和高大的锌柱一起，形成了一个地标——在夜晚发光的"灯笼"式天窗。

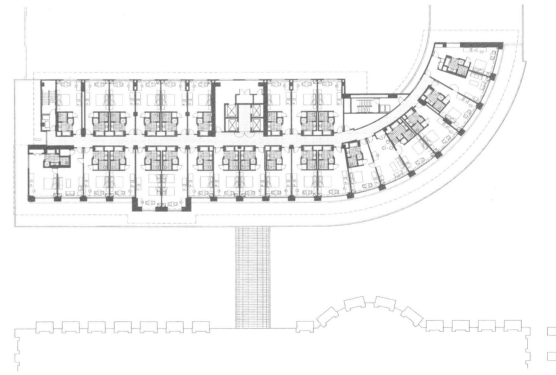

CENTURY CENTER

BEIJING, CHINA
北京，中国

世纪中心

Our passion to discover modern China, and to seek its opportunities, led us into a design competition for this commercial development, located on a prominent Third Ring site in Beijing's diplomatic quarter. The program of office towers and large hotel is one that is repeated throughout the city, with mediocre results stemming from the developers' common vision of Beijing as a purely international or "world" city, based exclusively on imported design. To their credit, most builders eschew trite variations on pagoda roofs, but we still hoped for some meaningful connection to the dense cultural history of China.

ART INTO PLANNING
In our previous work in the region—the master plan of Dong-Hwa National University campus in Taiwan, and our unselected competition bid for the Shanghai Grand Theater— we searched for insight not in architecture per se, but in art and landscape design. The plan of Dong-Hwa for example, was inspired by a scroll painting depicting at one point a small village and a nearby temple complex joined by bridges across a bend in the river. The everyday quality of the village and the auspicious nature of the temple are beautifully conveyed, and led us to a more overt sense of hierarchy and distinction between academic and residential areas of the campus plan.

ROCK INTO TOWER
For the Beijing project, the commercial program and planning limits suggested two towers and the hotel, which other competitors treated as a third tower, producing very similar designs. We had been impressed with the gnarled, columnar rocks—some nearly twen-

ty feet tall—that we saw in gardens in the Forbidden City. Like the vertiginous mini-mountains of Qui Lin in southern China, these grotesque forms seem uniquely Chinese, and a fine metaphor for a large-scale urban form. As the modeling of the office buildings proceeded, these shapes were abstracted in a nearly-symmetrical pairing of the towers into a single monumental form, whose gently bowed sides featured massive projecting volumes. At the cross-axis of the split tower a three-story bridge links the offices to the hotel.

HOTEL INTO ZOCALO
The urban benefit of the hotel is the public space it offers. Hotels throughout Asia provide extremely popular gathering places, for the public as well as the guests, and typically have a rich program of restaurants, entertainment, and shops. Thinking of Beijing's climate—hot and humid for half the year and dry, dusty and bitterly cold the other half—we organized the hotel as a mid-rise, with room floors wrapping three sides of a grand atrium—an acclimatized public square where the air is always clean. The relatively low volume of the hotel provides a yin-yang companion to the towers, strengthening the urban composition into two complementary forms set in a small urban park.

我们对探索现代中国以及寻求其中的机遇怀有很高热情，于是参加了这个在北京三环上外交区内一个显著地段上的商业开发项目的设计竞赛。写字楼和大型酒店的项目已经遍布全城，其平庸的结果应归咎于开发者们对北京的普遍构想——一个完全依赖进口设计的纯粹的国际化的"世界"城市。值得庆幸的是，大多数建筑师都避开了陈腐的大屋顶套路，但我们仍希望与中国深厚的文化历史建立一些有意义的联系。

规划中的艺术
此前在该地区的项目——台湾东华国立大学校园总体规划以及没有中标的上海大剧院中，我们本质上并不是在建筑上，而是在艺术和景观设计上寻求突破。比如，东华校园规划的灵感是从一幅卷轴画得来的，画中从一点看到一个小村庄以及附近的一组寺庙，两者由跨过河湾的桥梁相连。画面中，村庄的平凡特质和寺庙的喜庆特质得以巧妙地表达，这使我们对层次感有了更清楚的认识，也更明白地意识到校园规划中教学区和住宿区之间的差别。

塔楼中的岩石
对北京的这个项目来说，项目的商业性以及规划的限制暗示了其形式是两个塔楼加一座酒店，其余的竞赛参加者都把酒店处理成第三个塔楼，由此得出了非常相似的方案。而我们在故宫的花园里见到的粗犷的石体——有些将近6米高——给我们留下了十分深刻的印象。和中国南部桂林的令人眼花缭乱的小山一样，它们奇异的形态是中国特有的，而且在大尺度的城市形态中可以成为一个绝佳的隐喻。于是，写字楼的形态逐渐成形，在这一对几乎对称的塔楼里，这些奇异的形状被抽象成一个独特的不朽形式，那缓缓弯曲的侧轮廓表明了庞大的突出体量。在两座塔楼间的空隙处，一架3层楼高的桥连接着写字楼和酒店。

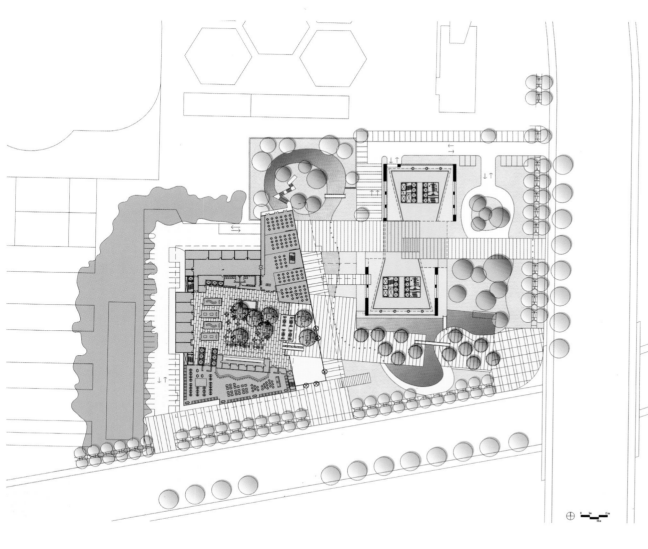

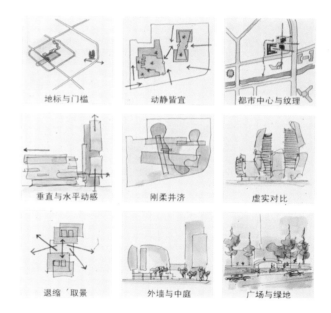

地标与门槛　　　动静皆宜　　　都市中心与纹理

垂直与水平动感　　刚柔并济　　　虚实对比

退缩´取景　　　　外墙与中庭　　　广场与绿地

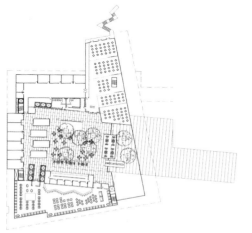

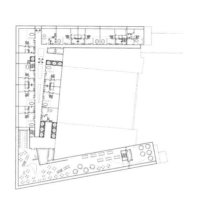

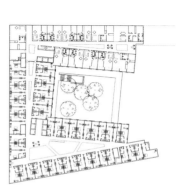

酒店成为基座

这个酒店为城市所做的贡献是它提供了公共空间。整个亚洲的酒店都极其热衷于提供向公众以及客人开放的聚会场所，并且一般都具有丰富的餐饮、娱乐和购物设施。我们考虑到北京糟糕的天气——上半年又热又潮湿，下半年则干燥、多尘且极度寒冷，决定把酒店做成中高层的，以客房形成三个面，围合着一个大中庭——一个调节气候的公共广场，其中的空气永远是干净的。酒店相对较小的体量也和塔楼形成一种阴阳对比，在一个小城市公园里把城市的组成成分加强为两种基本的形式。

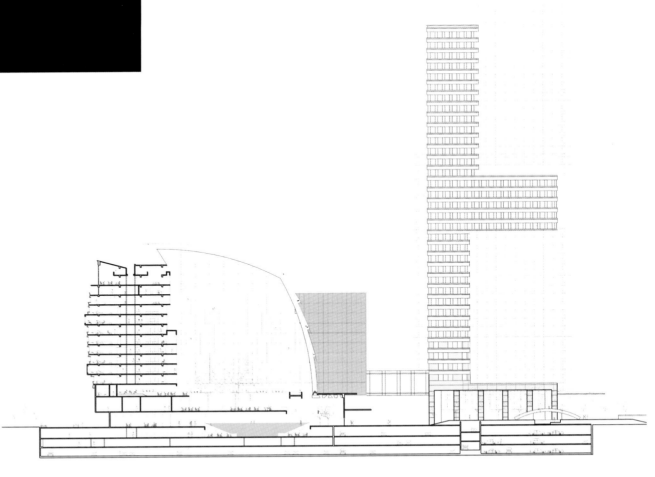

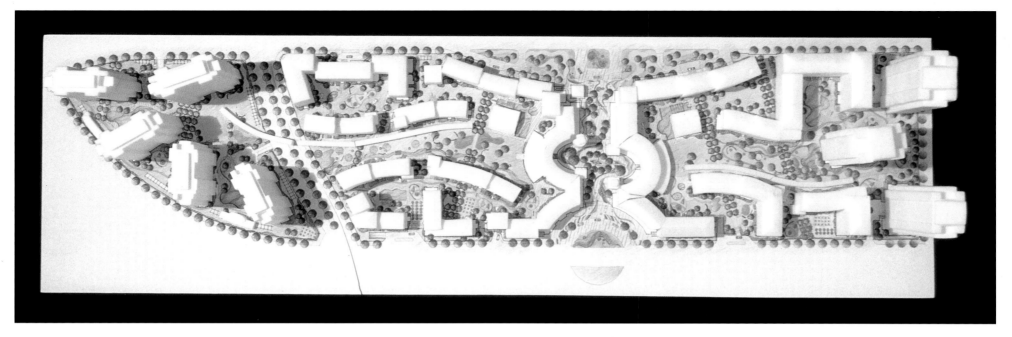

SERENDRA MASTER PLAN AND RESIDENTIAL/RETAIL

SERENDRA总体规划
住宅/零售区

Moore Ruble Yudell was commissioned by Ayala Land, Inc. to create a master plan for the Serendra Project, a 12-hectare site occupying the eastern section of the Fort Bonifacio Global City district (FBGC) in Manila. A major goal of the scheme has been to relate the new development to the existing master plan for the entire FBGC area, which is envisioned as an urban mixed-use expansion area for the nearby Makati Central Business District (MCBD), the country's premier business center. The site is intended for a mix of commercial and residential use for young professionals and families, organized into two residential sectors, High-End and Core-Mid.

The master plan concept aims to create a scale-friendly "garden city" celebrating human activity and interaction. A meandering sequence of open spaces and a low-density character was paramount throughout the design process. From the center of the site—a retail promenade—the density of the development rises in subsequent phases, to end at the north and south boundaries in carefully shaped residential towers.

RETAIL PROMENADE

A retail promenade serves as the main public space and nucleus of the project given its strong connection to the existing framework of the overall FBGC master plan and the adjacent commercial center "Market! Market!". The promenade is defined by façades that alternately project and recess, punctuated at vital points by towers. These towers function as gateways and markers along the promenade, creating variety and change. A two-story canopy articulates the retail spaces at the ground and second level throughout the promenade. Easy access to underground parking is provided by a central parking lobby as well as secondary access points at each end.

RESIDENTIAL BLOCKS

Building upon the tradition of European multi-unit housing, while respecting and adopting elements of vernacular Filipino style, a hybrid design was developed for the housing blocks. The blocks are typically configured as double-loaded, low to mid-rise structures in Phases I and II. The design avoids a feeling of repetition by allowing the blocks to curve in a sinuous fashion and breaking them at intervals with breezeways. This configuration allows a multitude of views and vistas throughout the entire site.

A hierarchical order of the façades has been achieved through a series of balcony elements and bay windows that use louvered screens to distinguish the various strata of the façade. Lanterns and monitors accommodating bi-level spaces provide a sense of movement in the roofscape of the buildings. Phase III will consist of high-rise condominium towers that are architecturally linked to the lower-density buildings.

The units vary in size and character depending on their placement and orientation throughout the site. Garden units, special rooftop and corner-tower units along with high-rise condominiums offer a wide variety of living experiences for tenants. The serpentine forms and configuration of the blocks provide views and vistas that are unique to each of the individual units.

MRY受Ayala Land有限公司委托，为Serendra项目作一个总体规划，地段占地12万平方米，占据了Bonifacio要塞国际城市(FBGC)的西侧部分。这个方案的主要目标是将新的开发与原有的整个FBGC区域的总体规划联系起来，这个原有的总体规划被构想为对附近的Makati中央商务区(MCBD，这个国家最主要的商务中心)的城市性混合功能延伸。地段被设想为商住混合的功能，对象是年轻的从业人员及他们的家庭。地段分为两个住宅区域，端部高层区和中部核心区。

总体规划概念的目标是创造一个具有友好尺度的"花园城市"，以展示人类的活动和交流。开放空间形成的蜿蜒序列及低密度的特性在整个设计过程中占据了主要地位。从地段中心的一个商业步行街开始，开发的密度在随后的阶段中逐渐上升，最终在南北边界处形成精心塑造的住宅塔楼。

商业步行街

商业步行街成为该项目的主要公共空间和核心，因为它紧密地联系着整体FBGC的总规和邻近的商业区"Market!Market!"所构成的原有框架。步行街的立面凹凸交替，在关键的点被塔楼打断。这些塔楼在步行街上发挥着大门和里程碑的作用，创造了多样性和变化。一个高两层的天棚覆盖着步行街上一层和二层的零售空间。地下停车场可以从中央停车休息室以及两端的次级通道轻松到达。

住宅体块

住宅体块以欧洲多单元住宅的传统为基础，同时尊重并吸取了菲律宾本国风格的元素，形成一个混合性的设计。在一期、二期里，体块的典型配置是双面走廊的低层至多层结构。为了避免重复感，设计中允许体块自由地弯曲，并不时用有顶的过道将之打断。这种配置进一步地带来了贯穿整个地段景色的多样性。

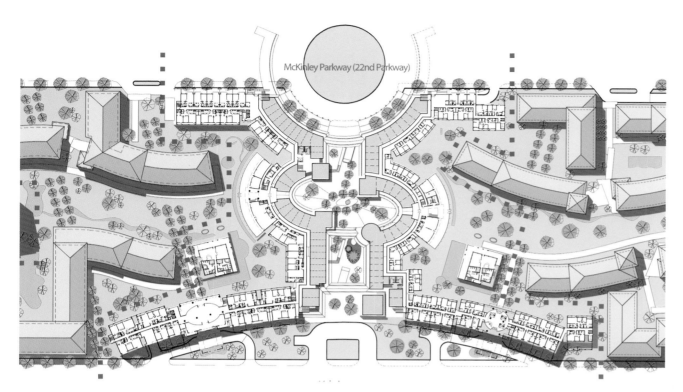

McKinley Parkway (22nd Parkway)

LANDSCAPE SPINE

The design gives high priority to the urban landscape, both in linking the project to the existing FBGC context, and in providing an important recreational amenity to the community. Beginning at the retail promenade lobbies, the Landscape Spine reaches out into both residential sectors, weaving through the residential blocks as a major organizing element to the design. A network of gardens branches off the spine, providing open space for clusters of residential buildings. These gardens are designed to focus pedestrian activity within and around nearby buildings, encouraging interaction and creating an attractive image for residential life. A specific landscape theme is proposed for each garden to establish character for each cluster and to add to the richness of the overall community. A number of amenities, including clubhouses, have been provided throughout the development for recreation and leisure.

一系列的阳台元素，与装有百叶窗以形成不同层次的凸窗一起，构成了立面的等级秩序。贯穿两层空间的灯笼式天窗和大屏幕为建筑的屋顶景观增添了一种动感。三期将由高层私有公寓的塔楼组成，它们在建筑上与低密度的楼群相连接。

单元在地段中的位置和方向决定了它们不同的大小和特征。花园单元、特殊的屋顶和塔楼转角单元以及高层公寓单元为住户提供了丰富多样的居住体验。建筑体块的蛇形的形态和配置方式使每个单独的单元都拥有独一无二的景致。

景 观 主 轴

这个设计把城市景观放在一个非常重要的地位，体现在项目与原有的FBGC环境之间的联系，以及为社区提供的一个重要娱乐设施。从商业步行街休息室开始，"景观主轴"向外延伸到两个住宅部分中，将住宅楼块编织起来，成为设计中的一个主要组织性元素。一系列花园形成主轴的分支，为住宅楼组团提供了开放空间。这些花园将行人活动聚焦在附近楼群的内部和周围，鼓励了交流互动，并描绘了一个动人的居住生活景象。每个花园都具有一个独特的景观主题，以确立每个组团的特性，并丰富整个社区。娱乐休闲开发中包含了一些便捷设施，比如社区会所。

RESORT DEVELOPMENT

Our design for this spectacular site in Southeast China strives to create a luxurious, family-oriented residential district that supports a natural and humane environment while offering hotel, retail, and leisure facilities to support a nearby entertainment and resort center.

FRAMEWORK OF THE MASTER PLAN: THE LOTUS BLOSSOM

The master plan is defined by a predominant orientation toward the entertainment center, creating an elegant oval that opens to the north. Evoking the image of a lotus blossom, the curve is anchored by taller landmark buildings that serve as "gateways' to the project. Optimizing views of the surrounding hills, the design envisions a sinuous, landscaped northern edge that engages the adjacent existing green zone along a main boulevard. The project's hotel and shopping zone is clustered in the "gateway" building at the northeast corner to relate closely to the entertainment center. The hotel combines stepped guestroom wings with a grand atrium, creating a harmonious interplay between indoor and outdoor spaces. The vehicular drop-off area along the main boulevard is layered between water-fountain walls that direct and welcome residents and guests into the clubhouse and hotel facilities.

THE CENTRAL LAGOON

A Central Lagoon serves as the social and recreational heart of the project, incorporating the metaphor of "three floating islands in a lake." It evokes a fantasy setting to enhance the project's resort atmosphere. A public promenade, accessed by pedestrian paths, encircles the Central Lagoon and is animated with landscaping, viewing terraces, bridges, and pavilions.

To the east, the Retail Island accommodates an outdoor restaurant and café above retail spaces that are easily accessed from the nearby Hotel. To the west, the Clubhouse Island incorporates its building as a special element in the landscape. The roof provides a park-like setting with pavilions, while the floors below accommodate a fitness spa and multi-purpose rooms. The indoor/outdoor infinity swimming pool is located adjacent to a tea house/restaurant with terrace seating and panoramic views of the entertainment center. The clubhouse's larger athletic and recreational spaces are located in a plinth below the inner ring of townhouses and villas that surround the lagoon. These spaces include a gymnasium, and tennis, basketball, and badminton courts. To the south, the Tropical Pleasure Island provides residents with recreational open space and a lower floor containing children's "discovery center" play areas. These public and private amenities are accessed by bridges, as well as glazed, underwater walkways that reinforce the nautical fantasy theme.

MAXIMIZING OPEN SPACE FOR LANDSCAPING

The master plan designates two concentric rings of buildings that echo the shape of an amphitheater. The lower inner ring consists of townhouses and villas, which are located on stepped terraces above the parking levels. The outer ring, lining the peripheries of the site along access roads to the south and east, contains high-rise buildings. These are designed in varying heights to harmonize with the hilly terrain around the site.

设计概念叙述
我们在东南中国一个观光地所作的设计力图营造出一个豪华、面向家庭的住宅区，它注重自然和人文环境，同时提供酒店、零售商业和休闲设施，并和附近的娱乐休闲中心相得益彰。

总体规划框架：盛开的莲花
总体规划由朝向娱乐中心的支配性方向决定，形成了一个优雅的向北敞开的椭圆形。项目的"入口"由几幢较高的地标式大楼锚定出一个曲线，令人想起盛开的莲花。为了使丘地周边的景致最大化，设计借助主大道原有的绿化区构想了一个蜿蜒曲折的景观化的北边界。项目中的酒店和购物区聚集在东北角的"入口"建筑中，与娱乐中心紧密地联系起来。酒店通过一个巨大的中庭与阶梯状的客房翼合并起来，在室内外空间之间建立了一个和谐的互动。主大道旁的机动车停靠区分散在喷泉幕墙之间，这些喷泉欢迎着来宾和房客，并把它们引向会所和酒店设施。

中央泻湖
中央的一个泻湖发挥着该项目的社交和娱乐核心的作用，并隐喻了三个悬浮"湖中的岛屿"。它所营造的梦幻般的环境增强了该项目的度假氛围。一条与人行道相连的公共散步道包围着这个中央泻湖，景观种植、观景平台、桥梁和亭台等为它带来了活力。

在东边，"商业岛"零售商业的上方有一个室外餐厅和咖啡厅，可以从附近的酒店轻松到达。在西边，"会所岛"将其建筑当作景观中的一个特殊元素。屋顶成为一个拥有亭子的公园似的环境，而下面几层则包含了温泉疗养区和多功能的房间。室内/室外无限泳池的附近有一个茶室/餐厅，从其平台式的座位上可以将娱乐中心一览无余。会所中较大的运动和娱乐场所则位于"内环"的下方基座中，"内环"围绕着泻湖，由联排住宅和别墅组成。这些空间包括了体育馆、网球场、篮球场和羽毛球场。在

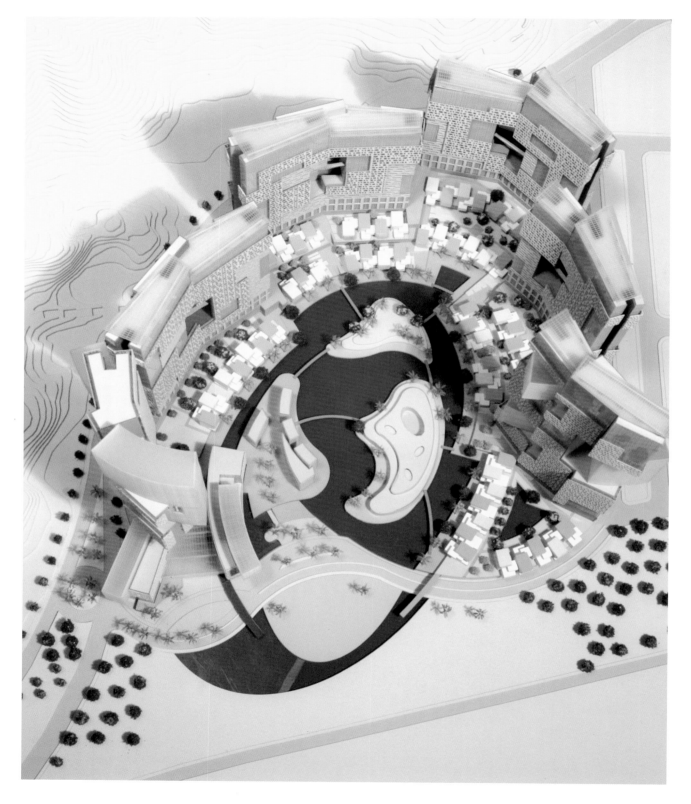

A palette of varying colors and materials provides individual identity and character to the townhouses, villas, and towers. The building bases have stone banding from the first to fourth floors, while the upper floors are treated with colored tiled walls. The façades lighten in hue as they rise up toward the sky. Large openings in the towers serve simultaneously as rescue floors and "sky gardens." These have bright accent colors to impart individuality to each tower. Syncopated bay windows and other glazed openings provide rich variety to the elevations, while lanterns add a sense of dynamic movement to the roofscape of the buildings.

RESIDENTIAL GARDENS AND TERRACES
A network of smaller, neighborhood-scaled gardens and courtyards provides welcome open space for residents on individual blocks and on the terraces above the parking levels. Together they form layers of intimate open spaces that complement and embrace the Central Lagoon.

SUSTAINABLE DESIGN STRATEGIES
Sustainable, ecologically-friendly features are optimized throughout the project. These range from green sod roofs and integrated photovoltaic systems to microturbines that generate on-site power. Water conservation methods include bio-filtration, wastewater management, and an overall strategy utilizing waterfalls and level changes that keeps water constantly moving. Lush native plants, trellises and canopies provide shade, while screens facilitate natural ventilation in the humid tropical climate of Southeast China.

南边，"热带欢乐岛"为房客们提供了娱乐性的开放空间以及一个低层建筑，里面设有为孩子准备的玩耍区"探索中心"。这些公共和私密的设施可以由桥梁到达，还可以通过水下玻璃通道到达，这些水下玻璃通道强化了航海幻想的主题。

营造尽量多的景观开放空间
总体规划中配置了两个建筑形成的同心圆，如同圆形剧场的形式。较低矮的内环由联排住宅和别墅组成，它们位于停车层平面以上的错落平台上。外环的东面与南面由高层建筑组成，形成了地段的外围。它们被设计成不同高度，与地段周围的丘陵地形取得了协调。

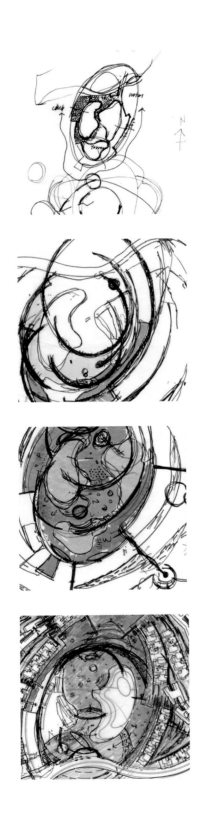

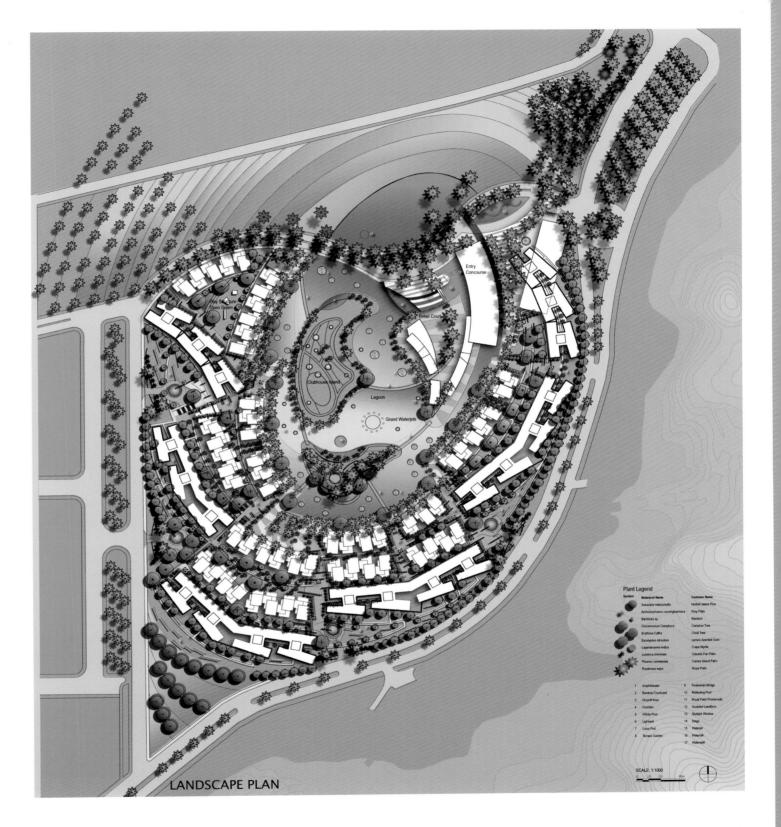

Plant Legend

Symbol	Botanical Name	Common Name
	Araucaria heterophylla	Norfolk Island Pine
	Archontophoenix cunninghamiana	King Palm
	Bambusa sp.	Bamboo
	Cinnamomum Camphora	Camphor Tree
	Erythrina Caffra	Coral Tree
	Eucalyptus citriodora	Lemon-Scented Gum
	Lagerstroemia indica	Crape Myrtle
	Livistona chinensis	Chinese Fan Palm
	Phoenix canariensis	Canary Island Palm
	Roystonea regia	Royal Palm

1   Amphitheater
2   Bamboo Courtyard
3   Dropoff Area
4   Fountain
5   Infinity Pool
6   Lightwell
7   Lotus Pool
8   Terrace Garden
9   Pedestrian Bridge
10 Reflecting Pool
11 Royal Palm Promenade
12 Sculpted Landform
13 Skylight Window
14 Stage
15 Waterjet
16 Waterfall
17 Waterwell

SCALE: 1:1000

LANDSCAPE PLAN

219

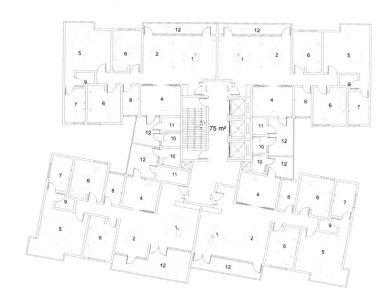

RESIDENTIAL TOWER
TYPE 3 (3BRLX + 3BRLX)

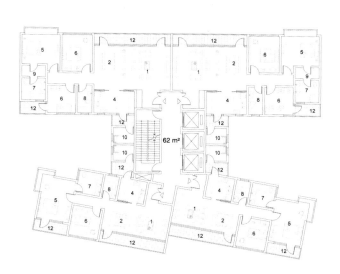

RESIDENTIAL TOWER
TYPE 4 (3BR + 2BR)

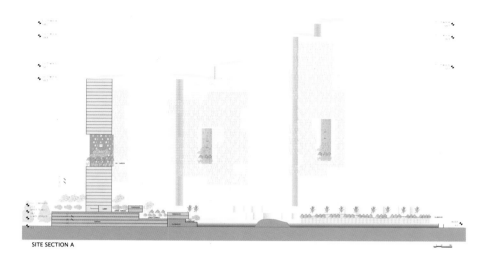

SITE SECTION A

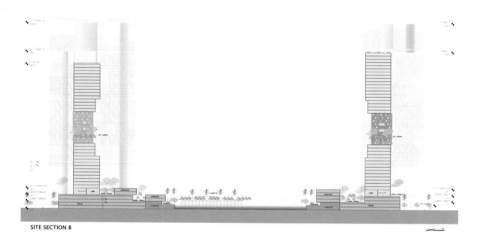

SITE SECTION B

一个变化多端的颜色和材料方案赋予联排住宅、别墅和塔楼各自单独的特征与个性。建筑底座的1~4层上有条石装饰，上面的楼层则配有彩色花砖墙。立面的色调在越接近天空时就变得越轻盈。塔楼中的大型洞口既可作为救援层，又形成了"空中花园"。它们具有明亮的浓重色彩，赋予每幢塔楼以独特个性。呈现出切分节奏的凸窗和其他玻璃开口为立面提供了丰富的多样性，而灯笼式天窗则为建筑的屋顶景观增添了一种动态感。

住宅花园和平台

一系列尺度亲切的较小花园和庭院为独立体块和停车场上方平台上的居民营造了一个受欢迎的开放空间。作为整体，它们形成了有层次的私密性开放空间，环绕着中央泻湖并使其变得完整。这些花园的目的是将行人的活动聚焦在附近建筑群的内部或周围，促进交流互动，并为居住生活描绘一个有魅力的景象。

可持续性的设计策略

在该项目中，可持续性和生态特征得到了最大体现。它们包括绿色植被屋面、综合光电系统以及现场发电的微型涡轮机等。水体储存方法包括生物过滤、废水管理以及一个整体性策略——运用瀑布和高差使水面不停地流动。茂密的本土植物、凉亭和天棚提供了阴凉，遮蔽物则在东南中国的热带气候下加速了自然通风。

TYPICAL ROOM PLAN   SUITE ROOM PLAN

HOTEL PLANS

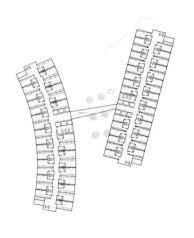

TYPICAL LEVEL PLAN

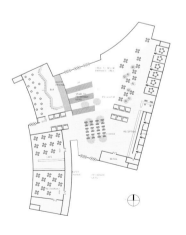

PROMENADE LEVEL PLAN

222

CHUN SEN BI AN MASTER PLAN + HOUSING

CHONGQING, CHINA
重庆，中国

春森彼岸总体规划和住宅群

Recent decades have witnessed a heavy migration of population from rural areas in China into the cities. With this migration comes an immediate and critical need for housing—there are now 31 million people in the area surrounding Chongqing, a city at the meeting of the Jialing and Yangtse rivers. The Chongqing City Planning Bureau selected our firm to create a master plan that provides 3,000 units of housing while thinking beyond our site to open and connect the city to the river. During lectures at Chinese universities, with extensive Q&A about how to build on and inhabit the river, we collected feedback from professionals, city planners, and students about what we can offer to the future of China. The resulting Chun Sen Bi An project is one of the largest riverfront urban developments in China, and will be an important catalyst for future river-adjacent development.

SITE ANALYSIS
The waterfront is Chongqing's greatest asset, yet previous development had blocked access to the river. Our master plan is the city's first major development to reach down to the river, opening and connecting to the water. The dramatically sloping riverfront location of the 13.8-hectare site affords views to the south across the Jialing River to the Yuzhong District of central Chongqing. The lushly vegetated site can be accessed by two roads, with a third new road that will connect the site with the newly developing Central Business District to the east.

CONNECTING TO THE NATURAL CONTEXT AND RIVER
The design draws significant inspiration from the prominent natural conditions of the Chongqing area, ranging from the nearby confluence of the Jialing and Yangtze rivers to the mountainous topography of the site and surrounding countryside. The Jialing River dominates the natural setting of the site, and the design takes advantage of both the riverfront location and steep slopes to provide views and connections to the water. The flowing movement of the Jialing is reflected in the curving shapes of the buildings, terraces, and paths which echo the ripples of water in the river.

Recent development in China has been at a rapid pace with a prevailing consciousness to demolish everything that currently stands. Our philosophy is to allow the past traditions of movement and memory of a place to inform the new plan. The defining framework of this design is a harmonious interplay of two major axes: a formal "urban" axis from town to river, and an informal "natural" axis that holds the memory of an ancient path.

FORMAL "URBAN" AXIS FROM TOWN TO RIVER
A formal axis in the center of the site directs pedestrians from the busy city street at the top of the project down to the waterfront. This spine represents the urban, public realm of the project, pulling the pedestrian flow down this central path and then laterally toward the east and west sides of the site, parallel to the riverbank. This public axis is animated by a grand flight of steps that echoes the traditional street-stairs in Chongqing and neighboring towns, and is punctuated by attractive terraces and viewing platforms. Retail shops are located on both sides of this central spine on the ground and second floors, adding to the lively urban character of the space.

最近几个世纪以来，中国人口经历了由乡村向城市的重大转移。随之而来的是对住宅直接且危急的需求——在重庆已经有3,100万的人口。重庆市规划办公室选中我们来为3,000个住宅单元做总体规划，同时，还希望越过我们的地段将城市向江边敞开并将二者联系起来。在中国大学的讲座中，我们通过大量的关于如何在江边建造和居住的问答，得到了来自专业人士、城市规划人员以及学生的反馈，得知我们能为中国的未来做些什么。最终的成果——春森彼岸项目，是中国最大的几个江滨城市开发项目之一，也将成为未来临江开发的重要催化剂。

场地分析
滨水地区是重庆最大的财富，但以往的开发阻断了通向江边的通道。我们的总体规划是城市中第一个向下延伸到江边，向江水开敞并与之相连的主要开发项目。这个13.8万平方米的急速坡降的江边地段提供了向南隔着嘉陵江看到重庆中心渝中区的景致。这个植被繁茂的地段可以由两条道路到达，而第三条新路将把地段与东边新开发的中央商务区连接起来。

自然文脉和河流的联系
设计中的大量灵感来自重庆地区著名的自然环境，从附近的嘉陵江与扬子江汇合点到地段及其周边农村中的山地。嘉陵江成为地段的主要自然环境，于是设计中充分利用了滨水区以及陡峭的山坡，提供面向江水的景色并与之建立联系。嘉陵江的流动感反映在建筑、平台和道路的曲线形式中，它们令人想起江水中的波纹。

近年来中国的开发是迅速的，但主导思想是拆除掉现存的所有东西。我们的观点则是让过去的运动传统和场所记忆来激发新的规划。这个设计的决定性框架是和谐互动的两条主轴：一条正式的"城市"轴线从城市通向江水，另一条非正式的"自然"轴线则保留住一条古代通道的记忆。

225

MRY是我在建筑史研究中一个很有意义的选题。这个事务所，是从查尔斯·摩尔的后现代主义开始启动的，我和这个建筑设计事务所有很好的关系，早在摩尔时代就去见过这个大师，摩尔之后，我再次去这个公司参观，认识了约德和乐伯，还有他们的高级建筑师詹姆士·马力·奥康纳(Principal James Mary O'Connor)等人。21世纪开始，我和他们甚至发展出比较密切的业务往来。他们承接了重庆龙湖地产公司在嘉陵江边的一个非常具有挑战性的高层建筑楼盘的规划和设计，那个地方原来叫做"陈家馆"，建成新住宅和商业区之后，将叫做"春森彼岸"。这个住宅区的设计，高度考虑到地形和历史的特点，从重庆的环境、气候、景观出发来探索，从设计图和模型来看，将是现代建筑的另一个突破点。该项目还获得了美国建筑师学会2005年的设计创意奖，我自己曾参与了这个项目的顾问性质的咨询工作。在和MRY的合作关系中，充实了自己的实践和教学经验，在我，也是有极大的收获的。

期望MRY在迎接未来的挑战中，更上一层楼，取得更大的成就。

王受之

从城镇通向河流的正式"城市"轴线

地段中央的一条正式轴线将行人从高处繁忙的城市街道引向低处的水边。这条轴线体现了该项目的城市性和公共性，引导行人沿着这条中央道路下来，然后与河岸平行地向地段的东、西端侧向移动。这条公共轴线由一段大阶梯激活，这段阶梯模仿了重庆及附近城市的传统街道阶梯，并辅有一些吸引人的台地和观景平台。这条中央轴线的两旁布置着1～2层的零售商铺，更增加了空间中活泼的城市特性。

非正式的"自然"轴线：古代通道的记忆

与正式的南北向轴线相呼应的是一条蜿蜒穿过地段的东西向非正式自然通道。这条非正式的通道保留了一条蜿蜒的我们称为"古代通道"的记忆，行人们沿着这条通道从港口走到高处的城市，已经走了几百年。沿着这条曲折、有机的步道，不时出现朝向各个方向的惊人景色，有的隐藏于建筑之间，有的则从眺望点向外开敞。这条非正式的有机通道在每个转折点都提供了戏剧性的景致，并且由植被繁茂的平台形成边界，它体现了项目的私密感和亲和感。

left: a vertical community along an ancient path

左图：垂直的社区沿着古老的街道

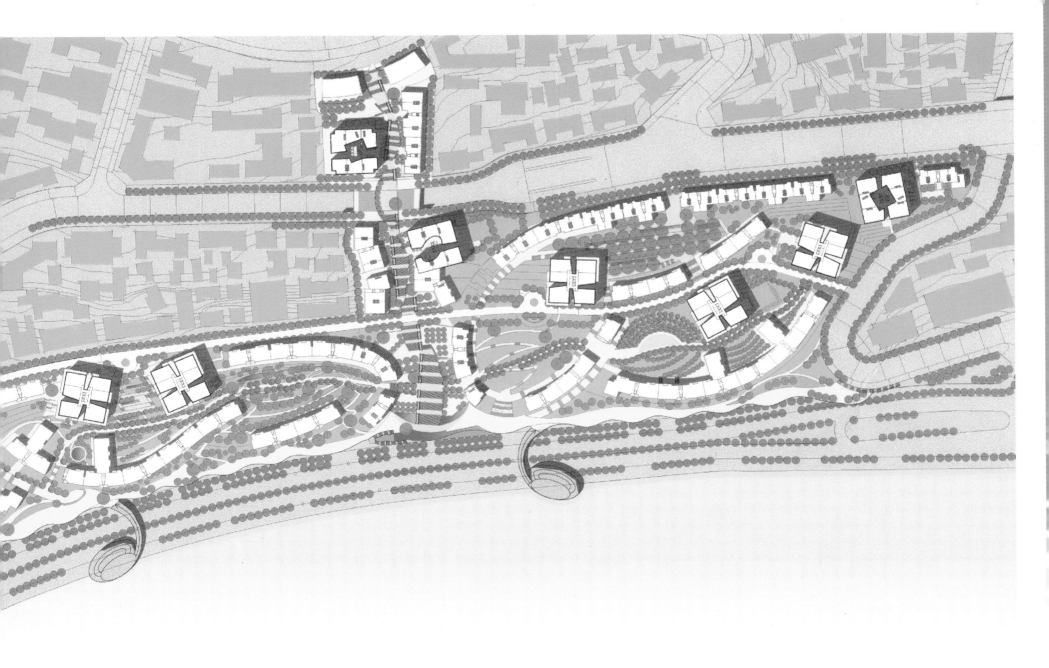

INFORMAL "NATURAL" AXIS MEMORY OF ANCIENT PATH

In counterpoint to the formal north-south axis is an informal natural path that meanders across the site from east to west. This informal path preserves the memory of the winding, "ancient path", as we have come to call it, which pedestrians have traveled from the port and docklands to the upper town for hundreds of years. Along this curved, organic walkway, surprising views are framed in all directions down to the river, sometimes concealed between buildings, and sometimes opening up from lookout points. Providing dramatic views at every turn and bordered by lushly landscaped terraces, this informal, organic path represents the more private and intimate realm of the project.

FIVE COMMUNITIES AT MULTIPLE SCALES

Five communities or neighborhoods will contain a mix of low, mid-rise, and tower buildings, with the distinctive identity and character of each neighborhood defined by the conditions in and around that neighborhood (central spine, waterfront promenade, upper or lower slope, city roads). Unlike a western low-density housing solution, these buildings must relate to Chinese high-density. Multiple scales of habitation, building massing, heights and spaces between buildings are carefully balanced to frame vistas of the Jialing River, and to lend human dimension to the project. The plan bridges the need for high-rise development by stepping the buildings up, like hills at the foot of mountains. The braided movement of the river connecting through the city and the reflecting movement of the water influenced the rotation of the high-rise towers toward different directions, and the lower and mid-rise buildings are curved to optimize views of the river.

A SYMBOL OF THE COMMUNITY

We are attracted to great streets not just as a destination of necessity but as a destination of leisure and activity. The monumental quality of the Grand Stairway becomes a city destination point in itself, a link between the upper town and the waterfront. A symbol of the community of Chun Sen Bi An, the Grand Stairway also provides a public amenity for the larger urban area. A sequence of escalators complements the stairs, providing easy access to the waterfront promenade along the southern edge of the site, immediately above a line of car showrooms and offices. The promenade, the Grand Stairway, a series of terraced plazas, and the opportunity for outdoor cafés all provide places for people to wander, socialize, and take in the activity of the street. This forms an attractive precedent for future developments along both sides of the river.

This new urban community can profoundly impact how the Chinese can live in the future, improving the quality of life in the entire region by providing sustainable solutions for living near the water, and bringing the body and memory back into architecture.

不同尺度的五个社区

五个社区，或者说街坊，将包含混合的低层、多层和塔楼，每个街坊的独特个性与特征由其内部和周围的环境（中央轴线、滨水步道、高处或低处的山坡以及城市道路等）所决定。与西方的低密度住宅方案不同，这些建筑必须满足中国的高密度要求。不同尺度的居住环境、建筑体量、高度以及建筑之间的空间得到精细的平衡，形成了嘉陵江的一个个框景，同时赋予该项目一种人性的尺度。为了达到高层开发的需求，规划中将建筑逐级升高，像山脚下的小丘一般。城市与嘉陵江之间辫状弯曲的联系以及江水的反射使得高层塔楼朝着不同方向进行旋转，而低层和多层建筑则为了获得最多的景色而弯曲。

社区的象征

我们被伟大的街道所吸引，并不仅因为那里有必需品，还因为那里有悠闲与活力。大阶梯的不朽性质使它本身成为城市的一个聚集点，一个高处城市与滨水地区间的联系。作为春森彼岸社区的象征，大阶梯还为更广阔的城市区域提供了公共便利设施。一系列的电动扶梯与楼梯形成互补，使人们轻松地到达地段南边界处的滨水步道，它紧靠在一排汽车样品陈列室和办公室的上方。步道、大阶梯、一系列台地广场还有室外咖啡场地都为人们提供了漫步、社交及参与街道活动的场所。这为未来江两侧的开发形成了有魅力的典范。

这个新的城市社区将深刻地影响中国人未来的居住方式，因为它提供了可持续的滨水居住方案，并将实体与记忆带回到建筑中，从而改善了整个地区的生活品质。

STUDIO PROFILE

约翰·乐伯

巴兹·约德

Moore Ruble Yudell Architects & Planners is an interdisciplinary design studio that is well known for an approach that extends to include the client. Founded in 1977 by John Ruble, Buzz Yudell, and Charles Moore, the partnership is based on shared humanistic values and a celebration of collaboration within the office and beyond to their clients and communities. Today, John Ruble and Buzz Yudell collaborate with a core group of principals and associates, many of whom have practiced together for more than a decade and continue the commitment to an inclusive participatory practice of a vibrant, engaged staff. Together, they have shaped the firm's humanistic and inclusive approach to design, translating their deep concerns for human habitation and interaction into the thoughtful development of unique solutions to an extraordinary range of places and projects.

Interpreting the role of architecture as a contributor to the more complex entity of place, and design itself as intrinsic to the act of habitation, they have persisted in asserting the value of the human dimension at every scale, from single-family houses to community-based planning, to civic, cultural, educational, and mixed-use projects in a diversity of settings. While respecting the roots of place and context, and the needs of human habitation, Moore Ruble Yudell strive equally for authenticity and originality.

John Ruble, FAIA
Partner

John Ruble began his career as an architect and planner in the Peace Corps, Tunisia, where a profound experience of culture, climate, and place provided lasting influences on his work. With Princeton, New Jersey architect Jules Gregory, he designed a series of award-winning public schools and civic projects before moving to California in 1974. With architecture degrees from the University of Virginia and the School of Architecture and Urban Planning at University of California, Los Angeles (UCLA), John has also been active in teaching and research, leading graduate design studios at UCLA and Cornell University. At UCLA, he studied and associated with Charles Moore.

Working closely with partner Buzz Yudell, John has helped to shape the firm's humanistic and inclusive approach to design, translating their deep concerns for human habitation and interaction into architecture and planning at many scales. As Partner-in-Charge, his work has spanned many years of projects in Germany and Sweden, such as Tegel Harbor and the United States Embassy in Berlin, and Potatisåkern and Tango in Malmö. He has also found great satisfaction in the firm's long-term relationships with university campuses, such as University of California, Santa Cruz, and the University of Washington's campus in Tacoma. As Moore Ruble Yudell's portfolio has expanded into new areas of expertise—from laboratories to courthouses—John has sought to make each work part of a broad, sustained exploration in the creation of place.

Buzz Yudell, FAIA
Partner

Buzz Yudell's passion for architecture grew out of a synthesis of artistic and social concerns. At Yale College his work in sculpture was complemented by exploration of the sciences and humanities. Graduate study at Yale expanded these commitments to a range of scales from small constructions *in situ* to urban design. It was at Yale that he began his long association with Charles Moore.

Buzz has collaborated intensively with partner John Ruble to expand the firm's expression and expertise to campus, cultural, civic, and residential architecture. His commitment to creating humane places inspired by climatic and cultural understanding has informed the firm's work at many scales. Buzz continues to be as interested in the design and crafting of lighting and furniture as in planning for urban infill or sustainable growth. His strong interest in the house as the quantum of community has helped to create a body of timeless residential work. As Partner-in-Charge, he has led projects in Asia, Europe, the Caribbean, and throughout the United States. His interest in nurturing community has found fresh expression on numerous campuses including University of California, Los Angeles, University of California, Santa Barbara, Cal Tech, University of Cincinnati, Dartmouth, and MIT.

Throughout his career, teaching, research, writing, and community service have been critical to the evolution and exploration of both the theoretical and physical role of architecture in shaping and celebrating place and community.

詹姆士・马力・奥康纳　　事务所总裁，亚洲项目总负责人

克丽斯特・贝克尔

詹尼・陈

James Mary O'Connor, AIA
Principal

Born in Dublin, Ireland, James Mary O'Connor received his Bachelor of Science in Architecture degree from Trinity College, Dublin and his Diploma in Architecture from Dublin Institute of Technology. As a Fulbright Scholar, he studied in Charles Moore's Master Studios at UCLA School of Architecture in 1982, and received his Master of Architecture.

As Principal-in-Charge, James has provided design leadership for academic, residential, and mixed-use urban projects, including Nishiokamoto Housing in Japan, Horace Mann Elementary School, and 606 Broadway housing in Santa Monica, California. His international focus is on large-scale housing, beginning with Potatisåkern and Tango in Malmö, Sweden. James is currently Principal-in-Charge of all Asian projects, including the Serendra mixed-use development for 5,000 housing units in Manila, Philippines, Chun Sen Bi An Housing in Chongqing, China, and Tianjin Xin-he New Town in Tianjin, China. James's interest in uncommon building types is reflected in the Sunlaw Power Plant Prototype, and the Santa Monica Civic Center Parking Structure, and he has led the firm in international design competitions such as the Beijing Century Center.

For over 15 years, James has taught design studios, lectured, and been guest critic at major schools of Architecture and Planning, including University of California, Los Angeles; University of Southern California; Southern California Institute of Architecture; University of Calgary-Alberta; University of Hawaii; Ball State University, Indiana; Hong-Ik University, Korea; and the following Architecture Schools in China: Tianjin University; Tongji University, Shanghai; Southeast University, Nanjing; Chongqing University; and Guangzhou Academy of Fine Art.

<joconnor@mryarchitects.com>

Krista Becker, AIA, LEED® AP
Principal

After graduating with honors from University of Southern California with a Bachelor of Architecture degree, Krista Becker practiced architecture at a variety of firms, gaining valuable experience with several project types, including civic, commercial complexes and high-rise towers, healthcare, multi-family housing, master planning, museums, and retail. Her ability to lead and coordinate complex client teams and multiple consultant groups, as well as her capacity for undertaking challenging project programs with attention to design, schedule and budget, has made her a strong influence in the advancement of Moore Ruble Yudell's management approach.

As the project manager and Principal-in-Charge for the United States Embassy in Berlin, the American Institute in Taiwan, the South Lawn Project at University of Virginia, the Law-Business Connection at University of California, Berkeley, and the recently completed Santa Monica Public Library, she has emphasized skillful communication and understanding, earning the confidence of some of the firm's most discerning client groups.

An active member of the American Institute of Architects, Krista is a guest lecturer and instructor at University of California Los Angeles Extension in the Construction Management Certificate Program.

Jeanne Chen, AIA
Principal

Jeanne Chen earned both a Bachelor of Science and a Master of Architecture degree from the University of Illinois, Champaign-Urbana, and joined the firm in 1989.

As project manager, Jeanne combines design sensitivity with skills in technical coordination throughout the design process, from the earliest program phases through documents and construction. At Moore Ruble Yudell, she has shown an affinity for large scale projects involving multiple user groups and detailed program requirements. Jeanne's ability to advance and develop the broad vision of each project while attending to client needs and technical detail has made her successful in leading complex institutional and civic projects, including major renovations and additions, such as the Hugh & Hazel Darling Law Library Addition at UCLA.

As Principal-in-Charge, her recent work includes master planning and design of academic and student housing projects for Dartmouth College in Hanover, New Hampshire. Jeanne directed Moore Ruble Yudell's team throughout the design and construction of the firm's largest civic project, the United States Courthouse in Fresno, California.

迈克·斯马丁

尼尔·松野

马利欧·魏里奇

Michael S. Martin, AIA
Principal

Michael Martin graduated with honors from the University of Illinois, Champaign-Urbana in 1976. In Denver, Colorado he became Principal Partner with The Aspen Design Group, where he focused on promoting sustainable architecture, including in the development of the Rocky Mountain Institute headquarters. He then joined Peter Gluck and Partners, New York, and later Kohn Pedersen Fox and Associates, where he worked on Canary Wharf in London, and the World Bank Headquarters in Washington, D.C.

After earning a Master of Architecture II degree from the UCLA School of Architecture and Urban Planning in 1993, Michael established his own Los Angeles firm. Since joining Moore Ruble Yudell in 1997, he has been Project Designer and Director on a number of large-scale academic and institutional projects including the Physical Sciences Building, University of California, Santa Cruz; Manzanita Village, an 800-bed student housing complex at University of California, Santa Barbara; The French Science Center, new and renovated scientific facilities at Duke University; and the John Brooks Williams laboratory and classroom complex for St. Edward's University, Austin, Texas. Michael has been one of the leaders of the architectural design effort for the mixed-use town center for Camana Bay on Grand Cayman, and has also guided the development of three new buildings, an administration building, cafeteria, and laboratory facility for a biotechnology company in Longmont, Colorado. With extensive design and technical experience on a wide variety of project types, Michael has managed all phases of project development from programming and conceptual design through construction documents, construction and commissioning.

Neal Matsuno, AIA, LEED® AP
Principal

Neal Matsuno joined the firm shortly after graduating from the University of Southern California in 1984. While leading projects, Neal combines design sensitivity with skills in technical coordination throughout the design process. His areas of special expertise include architectural lighting design. Neal has had a major responsibility for lighting design and technical detailing for projects including the California Center for the Arts in Escondido, Powell Library and Law Library projects at University of California, Los Angeles and the firm's residential projects.

He has been in charge of a number of institutional projects including the Walt Disney Imagineering Campus Master Plan and the National Tropical Botanical Gardens Library and Herbarium. Currently, Neal is the Principal-in-Charge of large scale projects involving multiple user groups and detailed program requirements, such as the Sloan School of Management project at the Massachusetts Institute of Technology, Glorya Kaufman Hall World Arts and Cultures Center at University of California, Los Angeles, and Camana Bay Town Master Plan in Grand Cayman.

Neal has won numerous lighting design awards for his work on the California Center for the Arts in Escondido including: the IIDA Edwin F. Guth Memorial Award of Excellence for Interior Lighting Design, the Lumen West Award for Lighting Design, and the GE Edison Award of Merit.

Mario Violich, ASLA
Principal

With a background in both landscape architecture and architecture, Mario's professional and academic experiences often fall within the transition zone where a building ends and landscape begins. Mario received his Bachelor of Landscape Architecture at University of California, Berkeley. He subsequently worked in landscape architecture and planning for the SWA Group in Sausalito and Laguna Beach. Wanting to broaden his design experience, he attended University of California, Los Angeles where he received a Master of Architecture degree in 1989. Mario joined Moore Ruble Yudell the same year.

Mario's design approach blends conceptual clarity and profound intuition. He has collaborated on a broad spectrum of projects ranging from master planning to institutional buildings, and numerous single family homes. His work as Principal-in Charge includes: the recently completed Joseph A. Steger Student Life Center at the University of Cincinnati, Ohio, the new Beth El Synagogue, Berkeley, California, and the National Tropical Botanical Gardens Library in Kauai, Hawaii. Single family homes include: the Ruddell Residence in Kauai, the Wasserstein Residence in Santa Barbara, California, the Falkenberg Residence in Woodside, California, and the Moir and Livermore residences, both in Monterey, California.

Mario is a member of the American Society of Landscape Architects, has been an instructor in the Department of Landscape Architecture at UCLA Extension since 1993, and an associate teacher at UCLA and UC Berkeley.

蒂娜 · 毕比

士丹利 · 安德森

Tina Beebe

Tina Beebe received her Master of Fine Arts from the Yale School of Art and Architecture. Working with Charles Moore as a student, Tina joined his firm in Essex, Connecticut and subsequently came to California to work with him in 1976. She also worked in the office of Charles and Ray Eames, learning much from her great friend and mentor, Ray Eames. As resident colorist and interior designer for Moore Ruble Yudell, Tina has integrated these influences with her extensive travel experiences to inform her choices for custom color and material palettes on commercial, institutional, and residential projects. She has provided consulting services for many distinguished architecture firms in the United States and abroad.

Tina's practice has expanded to combine her design and color abilities to include the design of gardens for residential and commercial settings. As plant material inspires her color palette, color evokes ideas for whole gardens, which in turn complement and enhance the color and materials of architecture. This unique approach is exemplified in her color and landscape design for the award-winning Tango Housing at the Bo01 Exhibition in Malmö, Sweden. Tina has successfully applied principles of color and landscape at an extraordinary range of scales, from her own house and gardens in Malibu and Sea Ranch, California, to the coloring of whole townscapes at Karow-Nord, Berlin, and Tianjin, China.

Stanley Anderson, AIA, IIDA
Senior Associate and Director of Interior Design

Stanley Anderson specializes in Interior Architectural projects and leads the Interior Design Studio at Moore Ruble Yudell as a Senior Associate. Most recently, Stanley has worked on the U.S. Embassy in Berlin as project manager and designer for the interior design of this 215,000-square foot U.S. Department of State building sited next to the Brandenburg Gate.

Prior to joining Moore Ruble Yudell, Stanley worked for the San Francisco offices of Brayton + Hughes, leading the interior design for such diverse projects as The Four Seasons Resort, Jackson Hole, Wyoming. His experience in all aspects of the design process, from Programming to Construction Administration, includes corporate, retail, hospitality, institutional and residential projects, ranging in scale from a 5,000-square foot custom residence to a 600,000-square-foot corporate headquarters. A partial list of Stanley's clients include Spiegel, IBM, Chiron, Four Seasons Hotels, the U.S. State Department, and numerous residential clients. Stanley has also designed and exhibited furniture in galleries and museums and designed products for national contract furniture companies.

Stanley Anderson graduated with honors and received his Bachelor of Architecture degree from the College of Architecture and Design at Kansas State University in 1985. He is a member of the American Institute of Architects and the International Interior Design Association. He has taught in the Interior Architecture Departments at the School of the Art Institute of Chicago and California College of Arts and Crafts.

SELECTED BIBLIOGRAPHY

Books by Moore Ruble Yudell

Webb, Michael. *Innovation in Sustainable Housing: Tango.* New York: Edizioni Press, Inc., 2005

Ruble, John and Buzz Yudell. *Moore Ruble Yudell: Making Place.* Sydney: Images Publishing Group, 2004

Ruble, John. "Libraries/Learning Centers." *Building Type Basics for College and University Facilities,* edited by David J. Neuman , New York: John Wiley & Sons, 2003

Koffka, Adrian and Wendy Kohn, eds. *Moore Ruble Yudell: Building in Berlin.* Sydney: Images Publishing Group, 1999

Riera Ojeda, Oscar, James Mary O'Connor, and Wendy Kohn. *Campus & Community: Moore Ruble Yudell Architecture and Planning.* Rockport Publishers, Inc., 1997

Riera Ojeda, Oscar and Lucas H. Guerra, eds. *Moore Ruble Yudell: Houses and Housing.* AIA Press, 1994

Steele, James, ed. *Moore Ruble Yudell.* Academy Editions, 1993

Books including Moore Ruble Yudell projects

Dickhoff, Anne. *Outdoor Rooms II.* Massachusetts: Quarry Books, 2006 (Yorkin House, Malibu, California)

The Phaidon Atlas of Contemporary World Architecture. London and New York: Phaidon Press, 2004. (Yorkin House, Malibu, California and Tango, Bo01 Housing Exhibition, Malmö, Sweden)

Yee, Roger. *Educational Environments.* New York: Visual Reference Publications, Inc., 2002 (Hugh and Hazel Darling Law Library Addition, UCLA)

Residential Spaces of the World, Volume 5. Sydney: Images Publishing Group, 2002 (Yorkin House, Malibu, California)

Slessor, Catherine. *See-Through Houses: Inspirational Homes and Features in Glass.* London/New York: Ryland Peters & Small, 2001 (Yorkin House, Malibu, California)

Trulove, James Grayson and Il Kim, eds. *New American House 3.* New York: Watson-Gupkill Publications, 2001 (Dodici Giardini, Pacific Palisades, California)

Trulove, James Grayson and Il Kim, eds. *New American Additions and Renovations.* New York: Watson-Gupkill Publications, 2001 (Gilbert House, Los Angeles, California)

Hardenbergh, Don and Todd S. Phillips, eds. *Retrospective of Courthouse Design 1991-2001.* 2001 (United States Courthouse and Federal Building, Fresno, California)

Cyberspace: the World of Digital Architecture. Australia: Images Publishing, 2001 (Sunlaw Power Plant)

Crisp, Barbara. *Human Spaces.* Massachusetts: Rockport Publishers, Inc., 2001 (Nishiokamoto Housing, Kobe, Japan)

Goslee Power, Nancy and Susan Heeger. *The Gardens of California: Four Centuries of Design from Mission to Modern.* Clarkson N. Potter, Inc., 2000 (Yudell/Beebe House, Malibu, California)

Langdon, Philip, *American Houses.* New York: Stewart Tabori & Chang, 1997 (Marine Street House, Santa Monica, California)

Riera Ojeda, Oscar, ed. *The New American House.* Whitney Library of Design, 1995 (Yudell/Beebe House, Malibu, California)

Ferguson, R. *Urban Revisions: Current Projects in the Public Realm.* MIT Press, 1994

Webb, Michael and J. Carter Brown. *Architects House Themselves: Breaking New Ground.* The Preservation Press, 1994

Sanoff, Henry. *School Design.* New York: Van Nostrand Reinhold, 1994

Steele, James. *Museum Builders.* Academy Editions/ Ernst & Sohn, London, 1994 (Hood Museum; Hollywood Museum, California; and St. Louis Art Museum, Missouri)

Toy, Maggie, ed. *World Cities: Los Angeles.* London: Academy Editions and Berlin: Ernst + Son, 1994

Johnson, Eugene J. *Charles Moore Buildings and Projects 1949-1986.* New York: Rizzoli, 1986

Street-Porter, Tim. *Freestyle.* New York: Stewart Tabori & Chang, 1986

SELECTED AWARDS AND EXHIBITIONS

American Institute of Architects Firm Award 2006

United States Institute for Theater Technology, PQ2007 Architecture & Technology Exhibition, Prague, Czechoslovakia: Clarice Smith Performing Arts Center, University of Maryland, College Park and Glorya Kaufman Hall, University of California, Los Angeles

AIA Santa Clara Valley Honor Award 2007: Horace Mann Public Elementary School

Berkeley Design Advocates Award of Excellence 2006: Congregation Beth El

Westside Urban Forum Westside Prize 2006: Glorya Kaufman Hall, University of California, Los Angeles

Royal Architectural Institute of Canada National Urban Design Award/Vancouver Award 2006: University Boulevard, University of British Columbia

AIA National Honor Award for Regional & Urban Design 2006: University Boulevard, University of British Columbia

Calibre Award for Environmental Leadership 2006: Santa Monica Public Library

Los Angeles Architectural Awards 2006, Sustainable category: Santa Monica Public Library

Southern California Development Forum Honor Award 2006: Santa Monica Public Library

McGraw Hill California Construction Best06, Best Civic/Redevelopment 2006: Santa Monica Public Library

Pre-cast Institute Design Award 2006 "Best Public/Institutional Building": Santa Monica Public Library

Chicago Athenaeum 2006 American Architecture Award: United States Courthouse, Fresno

AIA Committee on Architecture for Justice, Justice Facilities Review 2006-2007: United States Courthouse and Federal Building, Fresno

AIA National Honor Award 2006: Joseph A. Steger Student Life Center, University of Cincinnati

AIA/LA Merit Award 2005: Joseph A. Steger Student Life Center, University of Cincinnati

Westside Urban Forum Westside Prize 2005: 606 Broadway

AIA Ohio Design Award 2005: Joseph A. Steger Student Life Center, University of Cincinnati

AIA California Council Merit Award 2005: Joseph A. Steger Student Life Center, University of Cincinnati

Educational Facilities Design Award of Merit, AIA Committee on Architecture for Education (CAE) 2005: Joseph A. Steger Student Life Center, University of Cincinnati and Horace Mann Public Elementary School

Pre-cast Concrete Institute Design Award 2005: United States Courthouse & Federal Building, Fresno

AIA/LA NextLA Citation 2004: Chun Sen Bi An Master Plan & Housing, Chongqing, China

AIA Cincinnati Honor Award 2004: Joseph A. Steger Student Life Center, University of Cincinnati

Westside Urban Forum Westside Prize 2004: Santa Monica Civic Parking Structure

CMACN & AIACC Concrete Masonry Honor Award 2004: Horace Mann Elementary School

AIA California Council Merit Award 2004: Horace Mann Elementary School

Colorado Springs Partnership in Community Design 2003: Russell T. Tutt Science Center, Colorado College

AIA National Honor Award 2003: Bo01 "Tango" Housing

AIA California Council Merit Award 2003: Bo01 "Tango" Housing

Gröna Gårder Vilda Grännar award 2003 (landscaping/habitat): Bo01 "Tango" Housing

Council for New Urbanism Charter Award 2002: Tacoma Campus Master Plan & Phase I, University of Washington

Excellence on the Waterfront Honor Award, 2002: Bo01 "Tango" Housing

La Biennale di Venezia 2000: Bo01 "Tango" Housing at the Swedish Pavilion at Mostra Internazionale, Venice, Italy

Årets Stadsbyggnadspris 2001 (The Year's Building 2001): Bo01 "Tango" Housing

AIA National Honor Award for Regional & Urban Design, 1999: Tacoma Campus Master Plan & Phase I, University of Washington

AIA National Honor Award, 1998: Powell Library, University of California, Los Angeles

AIA/ALA Library Buildings Award, 1997: Powell Library, University of California, Los Angeles

Los Angeles Business Council Award, 1997: Powell Library, University of California, Los Angeles

Los Angeles Conservancy Award, 1997: Powell Library, University of California, Los Angeles

California Governor's Historic Preservation Award, 1996: Powell Library, University of California, Los Angeles

U.S. Foreign Building Operations, National Design Competition, First Prize, 1996: United States Embassy, Berlin

IIDA Edwin F. Guth Memorial Award of Excellence for Interior Lighting Design 1996: California Center for the Arts, Escondido

Lumen West Award for Lighting Design, 1996: California Center for the Arts, Escondido

American Concrete Institute, Winner in Architectural Category, 1995: Walter A. Haas School of Management, University of California, Berkeley

United States Institute for Theater Technology Merit Award, 1995: California Center for the Arts, Escondido

Stucco Manufacturers Association Bronze Award for Architectural Excellence, 1995: California Center for the Arts, Escondido

American Institute of Architects (AIA)/American Association of School Administrators, Citation, 1994: Walter A. Haas School of Business Administration, University of California, Berkeley

AIA California Council/National Concrete Masonry Association Award of Merit, 1994: Microbiology Research Facility, University of California, San Diego

AIA National Interior Architecture Award of Excellence, 1993: Nativity Catholic Church

State of Maryland, National Design Competition, First Prize, 1993: Maryland Center for Performing Arts, University of Maryland

Interiors Magazine 13th Annual Interiors Awards, Best in Institutional Design, 1992: Nativity Catholic Church

Interfaith Forum on Religion, Art and Architecture International Architectural Design Honor, 1992: First Church of Christ, Scientist

AIA California Council Urban Design Award, 1992: Plaza Las Fuentes

AIA California Council Firm of the Year Award, 1992

AIA Southwestern Oregon Chapter, First Place, Peoples' Choice Awards, 1992: University of Oregon Science Complex

AIA Southwestern Oregon Chapter Citation Winner, 1992: University of Oregon Science Complex

AIA California Council Honor Award, 1992: Yudell/Beebe House

California Institute of Technology, Invited Design Competition, First Place, 1992: Avery House

Arge Karow (Berlin) International Design Competition, First Prize, 1992: Karow-Nord Master Plan

Taiwan National Invited Design Competition, First Prize, 1992: Dong-Hwa University Master Plan

AIA/Sunset Magazine Western Home Awards Award of Merit, 1991-1992: Yudell/Beebe House

American Wood Council National Honor Award, 1991: First Church of Christ, Scientist

AIA San Diego Chapter Honor Award, 1991: Nativity Catholic Church

AIA California Council Honor Award, 1991: First Church of Christ, Scientist

AIA/American Library Council National Design Award, 1990: Humboldt Library

AIA Los Angeles Honor Award, 1990: Humboldt Library

AIA California Council Merit Award, 1989: House on Point Dume (Anawalt House)

AIA National Honor Award, 1988: Tegel Harbor Housing
AIA California Council Honor Award, 1988: Tegel Harbor Housing

AIA California Council Honor Award, 1988: Carousel Park

City of Santa Monica Mayor's Commendation, October, 1987: Carousel Park

Waterfront Center Excellence on the Waterfront Honor Award, 1987: Carousel Park

AIA National Honor Award, 1984: St. Matthew's Episcopal Church

AIA California Council Merit Award, 1984: St. Matthew's Episcopal Church

AIA Los Angeles Chapter Merit Award, 1984: St. Matthew's Episcopal Church

Architectural Record House of the Year, 1981: Rodes House

Santa Monica Pier Design Charrette, First Prize, 1981: Carousel Park

Tegel Harbor International Design Competition, West Berlin, First Prize, 1980: Tegel Harbor Master Plan

State of California Department of Rehabilitation Architectural Design Awards Program, "Building a Better Future Honor Award", 1987: Carousel Park

PROJECT CHRONOLOGY

1977–1979
Rodes House
Los Angeles, California

1979–1983
St. Matthew's Episcopal Church,
Pacific Palisades, California

1980–1985
Kwee House
Singapore

1981–1983
Marine Street House
Santa Monica, California

1981–1988
Tegel Harbor Phase I Housing
Berlin, Germany

1982
Parador Hotel
San Juan Capistrano, California (project)

1982–1989
San Antonio Art Institute
San Antonio, Texas

1983 competition
Center for Integrated Systems
Stanford University, California

1983–1987
West Wing Renovation and Decorative Arts Galleries,
St. Louis Art Museum, St. Louis, Missouri

1983–1989
Plaza Las Fuentes Mixed-use Development, Phase I & II
Pasadena, California

1984–1987
Inman House
Atlanta, Georgia

1984–1988
Humboldt Bibliothek
Berlin, Germany

1984–1993
Bel Air Presbyterian Church
Los Angeles, California

1984 competition; 1984–1987
Carousel Park, Santa Monica Pier
Santa Monica, California

1985–1988
Anawalt House
Malibu, California

1985–1989
Church of the Nativity
Rancho Santa Fe, California

1985–1989
Science Complex Master Plan, University of Oregon
Eugene, Oregon

1986–1988
Peter Boxenbaum Arts Education Centre, Crossroads School
Santa Monica, California

1986–1989
First Church of Christ Scientist
Glendale, California

1986–1995
UCSD Cellular and Molecular Medicine, East and West
University of California, San Diego

1987–1989
Walter A. Haas School of Business,
University of California, Berkeley

1987–1989
Yudell/Beebe House
Malibu, California

1987–1994
California Center for the Arts
Escondido, California

1988
Klingelhofer Diplomat Housing and Mixed-Use
Berlin, Germany

1988–1995
Chemistry Building, University of Washington
Seattle, Washington

1988–1996
Nishiokamoto Housing, Phase I and II
Kobe, Japan

1988–1996
Powell Library Seismic Renovation
University of California, Los Angeles

1988–2002
Potatisåkern Housing and Villas, Phase I & II; Phase III
Malmö, Sweden

1990 competition
Bolle Center
Berlin, Germany

1990–1993
Villa Superba
Venice, California

top center: St. Matthew's Episcopal Church; top right: University of Oregon Science Complex

中上： St. Matthew's Episcopal教堂
右上： 俄勒冈大学科学大楼

243

1991 competition
Friedrichstadt Passagen
Berlin, Germany

1991–1994
Schetter House
Pacific Palisades, California

1991–1998
Berliner Strasse Housing
Potsdam, Germany

1991–2003
Tacoma Campus Master Plan, Phase I and II completion
University of Washington, Tacoma

1992–1995
Dong-Hwa National University Master Plan Phase I
Hwa-Lien, Taiwan

1992 competition; 1992–1994
Peek & Cloppenburg Department Store
Leipzig, Germany

1992 competition; 1992–1996
Avery House, California Institute of Technology
Pasadena, California

1992 competition; 1992–1999
Karow-Nord Housing
Berlin-Weissensee, Germany

1992 competition; 1993–1998
Kirchsteigfeld Housing
Potsdam, Germany

1992–1994
Walrod House
Berkeley, California

1992–1998
Hugh & Hazel Darling Law Library Addition
University of California, Los Angeles

1993 competition
Kao-Shiung National Institute of Technology Campus
Master Plan, Taiwan

1993 competition
Lewis & Clark College Master Plan and Student Center
Portland, Oregon

1993–1996 competition
Konstancin Housing
Warsaw, Poland

1993–2000
Göttingen Master Plan
Bahnhof Westseite, Germany

1993–1998
Sherman M. Fairchild Library of Engineering and Applied
Science, California Institute of Technology
Pasadena, California

1994 competition; 1994–2001
Clarice Smith Performing Arts Center
University of Maryland, College Park

1994–1995
Playa Vista Office Campus Study
Los Angeles, California (project)

1994–2003
Wasserstein House
Santa Barbara, California

1995 competition
Stanford University Graduate School of Business
Residential Learning Center, Palo Alto, California

1995–1997
Kartanesí Winter Resort Hotel
Uludag, Turkey

1995–1998
Percival/Westbrook House
Newport Beach, California

1995–1999
Shmuger/Hamagami House
Pacific Palisades, California

1995 competition; 1996-in progress
United States Embassy
Berlin, Germany

1996–1997
Mustique House
French Virgin Islands (project)

1996–1997
Peg Yorkin House
Malibu, California

1996–1998
Elizabeth Moore House
Orinda, California

1996–1998
Gilbert House Remodel
Los Angeles, California

1996–1999
Graalfs House
Berlin, Germany

top left: Potatisåkern Housing; top center: Tacoma Campus Master Plan, University of Washington; top right: Hugh & Hazel Darling Law Library, UCLA School of Law

左上： Potatisåkern住宅
中上： Tacoma校园总体规划，华盛顿大学
右上： Hugh & Hazel Darling法学图书馆，加州大学洛杉矶分校法学院

1996-1999
Tiergarten Dreieck
Berlin, Germany

1996-2002
Regatta Wharf at Jackson's Landing, Phase I and II
Pyrmont, Sydney, Australia

1996-in progress
Camana Bay Master Plan, Mixed use, Retail and Cinema
Grand Cayman, British West Indies

1996-2006
United States Courthouse and Federal Building
Fresno, California

1996
Doris Student Housing, Tulane University
New Orleans, Louisiana (project)

1997-1998
Miramar Villas
Istanbul, Turkey

1997-1998
Nautilus Residences
Yesilyurt, Turkey

1997-1999
Baas/Walrod House
The Sea Ranch, California

1997-1999
Göttingen Office Building
Göttingen, Germany

1997-2001
Yudell/Beebe House
The Sea Ranch, California

1997-2002
Fairmont Towers Hotel Addition
San Jose, California

1997-2006
Interdisciplinary Sciences Building
University of California, Santa Cruz

1997-2002
Manzanita Village
University of California, Santa Barbara

1997-2006
Congregation Beth El
Berkeley, California

1998
House for the Next Millennium,
House Beautiful magazine (project)

1998-2000
Disney Imagineering GC3 Master Plan,
Glendale, California

1998-2003
Horace Mann Elementary School
San Jose, California

1998-in progress
MIT Sloan School of Management/SHASS/Dewey Library,
Massachusetts Institute of Technology, Cambridge

1998-2005
Russell Tutt Science Building,
Colorado College, Colorado Springs

1998-2002
Physical Sciences Building,
University of California, Santa Cruz

1999-2001
Tango, Bo01 Housing Exhibition
Malmö, Sweden

1999-2002
Science Building
University of Washington, Tacoma

1999-2005
The Falkenberg House
Woodside, California

1999-2004
Joseph A. Steger Student Life Center,
University of Cincinnati, Ohio

2000
Sunlaw Energy Corporation Power Plant
Los Angeles, California (project)

1999-2005
Glorya Kaufman Hall/Center for World Arts and Cultures,
University of California, Los Angeles

2000-2003
The Halprin House
The Sea Ranch, California

2000-2006
Watermark Condominiums
San Francisco, California

2000-2003
Biotechnology Development Campus
Longmont, Colorado

2000 competition; 2001
North Campus Master Plan, Dartmouth College
Hanover, New Hampshire

top left: United States Embassy, Berlin; top center: Peg Yorkin House; top right: Tango, Bo01 Housing Exhibition

左上：美国大使馆，柏林
中上： Peg Yorkin住宅
右上："探戈"Bo01住宅博览会

2001–2002
Inclusion Area D Faculty Housing Master Plan
University of California, Santa Cruz

2001–2007
606 Broadway
Santa Monica, California

2001–2007
Santa Monica Civic Parking Structure
Santa Monica, California

2001–2007
The Livermore House
Carmel, California

2002 competition
Beijing Century Center,
Beijing, People's Republic of China

2002 competition
United States Air Force Memorial
Arlington, Virginia (project)

2002–2006
Kemeny Hall & Haldeman Centers, Dartmouth College
Hanover, New Hampshire

2002–2006
McLaughlin Cluster Housing, Dartmouth College
Hanover, New Hampshire

2002–in progress
Serendra Master Plan and Residential/Retail
Fort Bonicafio City, Manila, Philippines

2002–2005
Western Asset Plaza
Pasadena, California

2002–2006
Santa Monica Public Library
Santa Monica, California

2002–2007
The Ruddell House
Kauai, Hawaii

2003–in progress
Tianjin Xin-he New Town Master Plan and Housing
Tianjin, China

2003–2006
John Brooks Williams Natural Sciences Center,
St. Edward's University, Austin, Texas

2003–2007
French Family Science Center, Duke University
Durham, North Carolina

2004–in progress
Chun Sen Bi An Master Plan & Housing
Chongqing, People's Republic of China

2004
626 Broadway
Santa Monica, California (project)

2004–in progress
West Village Implementation Plan
University of California, Davis

2004–in progress
Law-Business Connection
University of California, Berkeley

2005 competition
University Boulevard, University of British Columbia
Vancouver, British Columbia, Canada

2005
North Houses Study, California Institute of Technology
Pasadena, California

2005–in progress
Moir House
Carmel, California

2005–in progress
Class of 1953 Commons, Dartmouth College
Hanover, New Hampshire

2005–in progress
Amber Bay Housing
Dalian, People's Republic of China

2005–in progress
Law-Business Connection
University of California, Berkeley

2005–in progress
South Lawn Project, University of Virginia
Charlottesville, Virginia

2005–in progress
American Institute in Taiwan
Taipei, Taiwan

2006–in progress
Baxter Hall Study, California Institute of Technology
Pasadena, California

2006–in progress
Resort Development
Southeast China

top left: Manzanita Village, University of California, Santa Barbara;
top center: United States Courthouse, Fresno; top right: Chun Sen
Bi An Master Plan & Housing

左上：Manzanita 村，加州大学圣芭芭拉分校
中上：美国联邦法院，弗雷斯诺
右上：春森彼岸总体规划及住宅

PROJECT CREDITS

YUDELL/BEEBE HOUSE
The Sea Ranch, California

Client: Buzz Yudell and Tina Beebe
Architect: Moore Ruble Yudell Architects & Planners
Principal-in-Charge: Buzz Yudell
Associate-in-Charge: Marc Schoeplein
Color and Materials: Tina Beebe
Landscape: Tina Beebe
Lighting: Buzz Yudell
Project Team: Tim Eng, Scott Walter, Ed Diamante
Models: Mark Grand, Vincent Matthew, Michael O'Bryan
Watercolor site plan: Tina Beebe
Photographer: Kim Zwarts

PEG YORKIN HOUSE
Malibu, California

Client: Peg Yorkin, David Yorkin, and Nicole Yorkin
Architect: Moore Ruble Yudell Architects & Planners
Partner-in-Charge: Buzz Yudell
Collaborating Partner: John Ruble
Associate-in-Charge: Marc Schoeplein
Color and Materials: Tina Beebe
Lighting: Neal Matsuno
Landscape: Tina Beebe, Mario Violich
Project Team: Tim Eng, Ed Diamante, Bob Anderson, Don Aitken, Scott Walter, Michael Martin, Mariana Boctor, Stephen Penhoet, Christian Daniels
Models: Mark Grand, Ken Pai
Photographer: Kim Zwarts

TANGO, BO01 HOUSING EXHIBITION
Malmö, Sweden

Client: MKB Fastighets AB
Design Architect: Moore Ruble Yudell Architects & Planners with FFNS Architects
Partner-in-Charge: John Ruble

Collaborating Partner: Buzz Yudell
Principal-in-Charge: James Mary O'Connor
Color and Materials: Tina Beebe, Kaoru Orime
Project Team: Lisa Belian, Tony Tran
Interior Design, Exhibition Apartment: Tina Beebe, Kaoru Orime
Landscape Design: John Ruble, James Mary O'Connor, Tina Beebe, Kaoru Orime
Models: Mark Grand, Chad T. Takenaka, Vely Zajec, Don Hornbeck, Joshua Lunn, Matthew Vincent, Lance Collins
Digital Renderings: Ross Morishige

Executive Architect: SWECO FFNS Arkitekter AB
Principal: Bertil Öhrström
Project Architects: Karin Bellander, Lars Lindahl
Landscape Architect: Siv Degerman
Interior Designers: Karin Bellander, Johanna Wittenmark
Project Management: SWECO Projektledning AB
Project Manager: Pär Hammarberg; Assistant Project Manager and IT Coordinator: Conny Nilsson
Photographers: Werner Huthmacher, Ole Jais

AMBER BAY RESORT
Dalian, People's Republic of China

Client: Dalian Amber Bay Development Co., Ltd.
Shareholders: Parkland Group Co., Ltd. & Union Trust
General Manager: Liu Lijun
Design Architect: Moore Ruble Yudell Architects & Planners
Partners: John Ruble, Buzz Yudell
Principal-in-Charge: James Mary O'Connor
Project Team: Halil Dolan, Pooja Bhagat, Tony Tran, Nozomu Sugawara, Takuji Mukaiyama, Toru Narita, Clay Holden, Michael Heise
Models: Toru Narita, Nozomu Sugawara, Kentaro Yamada

Master Planner/Landscape Architect: SWA Group, Houston (Kevin Shanley, Peiwen Yu)
Collaborating Architect: Graft-Beijing (Gregor Hoheisel, Waterfront Commercial Center)

MANZANITA VILLAGE
University of California, Santa Barbara

Client: UCSB Design & Construction/Capital Programs
Design Architect: Moore Ruble Yudell Architects & Planners
Partner-in-Charge: Buzz Yudell
Collaborating Partner: John Ruble
Principal-in-Charge: Michael S. Martin
Project Manager: Richard Destin
Color and Materials: Tina Beebe, Kaoru Orime
Lighting: Neal Matsuno
Project Team: Ed Diamante, Alberto Reano, Ted Kane, Laurie Groehler, Oliver Matla, Stephen Penhoet, Ken Kim, Katherine Yi, Murat Sanal, David Ellien
Models: Mark Grand, Donald Hornbeck, Joshua Lunn, Vely Zajec, Michael O'Bryan
Renderings: Al Forster, Tony Tran

Executive Architect: DesignARC, Santa Barbara
Principal-in-Charge: J. Michael Holliday
Project Managers: Bruce Bartlett, Steve Carter
Photographers: Werner Huthmacher, Art Gray

POTATISÅKERN HOUSING
Malmö, Sweden

Client: Skanska Nya Hem, Phase I & II: HSB Malmö, Phase III: MKB Fastighets AB, Phase IV
Design Architect: Moore Ruble Yudell Architects & Planners
Partners: John Ruble, Buzz Yudell, Charles Moore
Principal-in-Charge: James Mary O'Connor (Phases II, III, and IV)
Associate-in-Charge: Cecily Young (Phase I)
Associate-in-Charge: Renzo Zecchetto (Concept Phase)

Project Team:
Phases II, III & IV: Lisa Belian, Izzet Motola, Adam Padua, Tony Tran, Roger Lopez, Erin Hillhouse, Ken Kim, Alberto Reano
Phase 1: Ying-Chao Kuo, Chris Duncan, Tea Sapo, Yeon Keun Jeong, Mary Beth Elliott, Steven Gardner, John Taft, Tony Tran, James Mary O'Connor, Wing-Hon Ng
Landscape Design: John Ruble, Cecily Young, James Mary O'Connor, Tina Beebe
Models: Mark Grand, Craig Currie, Matthew Vincent, Dirk Schoerner
Renderer: George Nakatani

Associate & Executive Architect:
Phase 1 and II: SWECO/FFNS Arkitekter, Malmö with Hultin & Lundquist Arkitekter
SWECO/FFNS
Principal-in-Charge: Bertil Öhrström
Project Manager: Lars Lindahl
Hultin & Lundquist:
Principal-in-Charge: Kurt Hultin
Project Manager: Dennis Johnsson
Phase II (Villas): Hultin & Lundquist Arkitekter AB
Principal-in-Charge: Kurt Hultin
Project Manager: Dennis Johnsson
Phase III (HSB Building): Mernsten Arkitektkontor AB
Principal-in-Charge: Bertil Mernsten
Hultin & Lundquist Arkitekter AB
Principals: Kurt Hultin, Dennis Johnsson
Phase IV: SWECO/FFNS Arkitekter AB
Principal-in-Charge: Bertil Öhrström
Project Manager: Lars Lindahl
Project Team: Maria Listrup, Cecilia Spannel, Bengt-Åke Jarnestad, Charlotta Rosén

Executive Landscape Architect: Pr MarkDesign
Principal-in-Charge: Per Renwart
Photographers: Werner Huthmacher, Lars Finnström, Lars Mongs

TIANJIN XIN-HE MASTER PLAN & HOUSING
Tianjin, People's Republic of China

Client: Sunco Investment, Inc.
Design Architect: Moore Ruble Yudell Architects & Planners
Partners: John Ruble, Buzz Yudell
Principal-in-Charge: James Mary O'Connor
Color and Materials: Tina Beebe, Kaoru Orime, Yana Khudyakova
Project Team: Halil Dolan, Tim Feigenbutz, Pooja Bhagat, Therese Kelly, Simone Barth, Tony Tran, Matthew Blake, Alexander Matthies, Michael König, Laura Flotho, Martin Sonnenberg
Models: John Leimbach, Veronica Vela, Mark Grand, Tim Feigenbutz, Carissa Shrock
Research: Janet Sager, Rebecca Bubenas

Associate Architect: Yang Architects
Principal-in-charge: Akai Ming-Kae Yang
Project Team: Nicolas Rousset, Kristina Hahn, Jan Lepicovsky, Xiao-Yan Sun, Lin-Qi Mei, Qi Li, Yin Li
Landscape Architect: EDAW

CAMANA BAY
Grand Cayman Island, British West Indies

Client: Cayman Shores Development Ltd.
Design Architect: Moore Ruble Yudell Architects & Planners
Partner-in-Charge: Buzz Yudell
Collaborating Partner: John Ruble
Principals-in-Charge: Michael S. Martin, Neal Matsuno
Project Manager: Anthony Wang
Technical Coordinator/Associate: Martin Saavedra
Color and Materials: Tina Beebe, Kaoru Orime
Interior Design: Stanley Anderson
Project Team: Kinneret Atia, Dan Bajor, Krista Becker, Matt Blake, Mark Bittoni, David Cutler, Michael de Villiers, Richard Destin, Tim Eng, Jeanne Fitzgerald, Bernardo Frias, Laurie Groehler, Anton Henning, Chris Hamilton, Clay Holden, Chris Jonick, Andrew Kao, Therese Kelly, Yana Khudyakova, Sang Dae Lee, Frank Maldonado, Tomohisa Miyauchi, Ross Morishige, Takuji Mukaiyama, Amy Newborn, Wing-Hon Ng, Daniela Oberherr, Oscar Pineda, Alberto Reano, Amy Sklar, Kirk Soderstrom, Carissa Shrock, Nozomu Sugawara, John Theeuwes, Charlotte Thomas, Tony Tran, Matt Vincent, Vely Zajec
Models: Mark Grand, Philippe Arias, Jed Bunkowski, Chad Chistopher, Joel Chappo, Benjamin Forster, Michael Heise, Matt MacDonald, Veronica Vela, Nate Wade, Nicholas Worden
Renderer: Al Forster

Consulting Architects: Burns Conolly Group Limited
Executive Architects: Spillis Candella DMJM
Landscape Architects: Olin Partnership
Lighting Consultants: L'Observatoire International, Lighting Designers
Signage and Graphics: Sussman Prejza & Company, Inc.

UNITED STATES COURTHOUSE
Fresno, California

Client: General Services Administration
Design Architect: Moore Ruble Yudell Architects & Planners
Partner-in-Charge: John Ruble
Collaborating Partner: Buzz Yudell
Principal-in-Charge: Jeanne Chen
Associate: Bob Dolbinski
Color and Materials: Tina Beebe, Kaoru Orime
Project Team: Chris Hamilton, Tim Eng, Ross Morishige, Roger Lopez, Tony Tran
Models: Mark Grand, Vely Zajec, Joshua Lunn, Matthew Vincent
Renderer: Doug Jamieson
Digital Illustration: Ross Morishige

Executive Architect: Gruen Associates
Principal-in-Charge: Debra Gerod, Mike Enomoto
Landscape Architect: Pamela Burton & Company
Interiors: Brayton & Hughes Design Studio
Artists: Anna Valentina Murch and Douglas Hollis
Photographer: Tim Griffith

SANTA MONICA PUBLIC LIBRARY
Santa Monica, California

Client: City of Santa Monica
Architect: Moore Ruble Yudell Architects & Planners
Partner-in-Charge: John Ruble
Collaborating Partner: Buzz Yudell
Principal-in-Charge/Project Manager: Krista Becker
Associate: Michael de Villiers
Color and Materials: Tina Beebe, Yana Khudyakova, Kaoru Orime
Project Team: Haekwan Park, Clay Holden, Richard Destin, Bob Dolbinski, Carissa Shrock, Neal Matsuno, Oscar Pineda, Bernardo Frias, JT Theeuwes, Martin Saavedra, Simone Barth, Krista Scheib, Gerardo Rivero, Henry Lau

Landscape: Pamela Burton & Co.
Interior Furnishings: CNI Design
Lighting: Patrick B. Quigley & Associates
Photographer: John Edward Linden

SANTA MONICA CIVIC PARKING STRUCTURE
Santa Monica, California

Client: The City of Santa Monica
Design Architect: Moore Ruble Yudell Architects & Planners
Partner-in-Charge: John Ruble
Collaborating Partner: Buzz Yudell
Principal-in-Charge: James Mary O'Connor
Color and Materials: Tina Beebe, Kaoru Orime
Project Team: Halil Dolan, Tim Feigenbutz, Haruyuki Yokoyama, Tony Tran
Models: Mark Grand, Halil Dolan

Executive Architect: International Parking Design
(Don Marks, Dirmali Botejue)
Contractor: ARB, Inc.
Landscape Architect: Melendrez Design Partners
Lighting Consultant: Francis Krahe & Associates
Artist: Mark Lere
Photographer: Images by: BrubakerPhotography.com

CLARICE SMITH PERFORMING ARTS CENTER
University of Maryland, College Park

Client: Engineering and Architectural Services, University of Maryland
Design Architect: Moore Ruble Yudell Architects & Planners
Principal-in-Charge: Buzz Yudell
Principal: John Ruble
Project Director: Jim Morton
Senior Associate-in-Charge: James Mary O'Connor
Color and Materials: Tina Beebe
Project Managers: Hong Chen, Denise Haradem, Martin Saavedra
Competition Team: Celina Welch, Bob Anderson, Erica Moon, Daniel Garness, Shuji Kurokawa, Akai Ming-Kae Yang, Mark Peacor, Tony Tran, Mario Violich, Adrian Koffka, Adam Padua
Project Team: Harry Steinway, Mary Jane Kopitzke, Alfeo B. Diaz, Erica Moon, Bob Anderson, Adam Padua, Kaz Baba, Wendy Kohn, Akai Ming-Kae Yang, Richard Williams, Amy Alper, Holly Bieniewski, Michael Xu, Christine Cho, Thurman Grant, Mary Beth Elliott, Sara Loe, Angel Gabriel, Will Shepphird, Tony Tran
Models: Mark Grand, Chris Roades, Craig Currie
Renderers: Al Forster, Daniel Garness

Associate Architect: Ayers/Saint/Gross Architects
Principal-in-Charge: Richard Ayers
Project Team: Adam Gross, George Thomas, Duncan Kirk, John Dale, Peter Garver
Landscape Architect: Michael Vergason Landscape
Theater Consultants: Theater Projects Consultants, Inc
Acoustical Consultants: R Lawrence Kirkegaard & Associates
Interior Furnishings: Audrey Alberts Design
Lighting: David A. Mintz
Photographers: Alan Karchmer, Werner Huthmacher, Jim Simmons

THE JOSEPH A. STEGER STUDENT LIFE CENTER
University of Cincinnati, Ohio

Client: Campus Planning, University of Cincinnati
Design Architect: Moore Ruble Yudell Architects & Planners
Partner-in-Charge: Buzz Yudell
Collaborating Partner: John Ruble
Principal-in-Charge: Mario Violich
Project Manager: Adam Padua
Color and Materials: Tina Beebe, Kaoru Orime, Yana Khudyakova
Project Team: Bob Dolbinski, Alberto Reano, Ted Kane,

Alexis Bennett, Ross Morishige
Models: Mark Grand, Don Hornbeck
Digital Illustrations: Ross Morishige and glaserworks
Associate Architect: glaserworks
Principal-in-Charge: Arthur A. Hupp
Principal: Michael J. Moose
Principal/Project Manager: Steve Haber
Project Team: Michael Maltinsky, Scott Layman
Master Plan/Landscape Architect: Hargreaves
Associates; Design Director: George Hargreaves
Principals-in-Charge: Mary Margaret Jones, Glenn Allen
Environmental Graphic Design: Kolar Design Inc. and
Marcia Shortt Design
Interior Design: Design Details, Inc.
Photographers: Ron Pollard, Alan Karchmer

HORACE MANN ELEMENTARY SCHOOL
San Jose, California

Client: San Jose Unified School District
The Redevelopment Agency of the City of San Jose
Design Architect: Moore Ruble Yudell Architects & Planners
Partner-in-Charge: John Ruble
Collaborating Partner: Buzz Yudell
Principal-in-Charge: James Mary O'Connor
Color and Materials: Tina Beebe, Kaoru Orime
Project Manager: Adam Padua
Project Team: Alberto Reano, Lisa Belian, Ed Diamante,
Roger Lopez, Martin Saavedra, Tony Tran
Models: Mark Grand, Matthew Vincent,
Vely Zajec, Lance Collins
Renderer: Al Forster
Photographer: John Linden, Art Gray, Alan Karchmer

Executive Architect: BFGC Architects Planners Inc.
Project Manager: David Cartnal
Landscape Architect: Pamela Burton & Co.

UNIVERSITY BOULEVARD COMPETITION
University of British Columbia, Vancouver, Canada

Design Architect: Moore Ruble Yudell Architects & Planners
Partner-in-Charge: Buzz Yudell
Collaborating Partner: John Ruble
Principal-in-Charge: Jeanne Chen
Project Team: Clay Holden, JT Theeuwes,
Bob Dolbinski, Adam Padua, Tomohisa Miyauchi,
Carissa Shrock, Sang Dae Lee, Laurie Groehler,
Ken Kim, Wing-Hon Ng, Stanley Anderson, Tony Tran,
Andrew Kao, Mark Grand, Tina Beebe

Associate Architect: Hughes Condon Marler, Vancouver
Design Landscape Architect: Olin Partnership
Local Landscape Architect: Phillips Farvaag Smallenberg
Water Color Renderings: Al Forster
Eco-stream Renderings: Olin Partnership
Computer Animation: Charles Hellwig
Photography: Jim Simmons
Model: Model Concepts

BIOTECHNOLOGY DEVELOPMENT CAMPUS
Longmont, Colorado

Design Architect: Moore Ruble Yudell Architects & Planners
Partner-in-Charge: John Ruble
Collaborating Partner: Buzz Yudell
Project Architect: Michael S. Martin
Administration/Cafeteria Facilities
Project Manager: Adrian Koffka
Project Team: Laurie Groehler, Alberto Reano, Chris
Hamilton, Oliver Matla, Roger Lopez
Process Engineering/Analytical Laboratory/Offices
Project Managers: Wing-Hon Ng, Adam A. Padua
Project Team: Chris Hamilton, Roger Lopez, Richard
Destin, Sager Chavan, Bill Ferehawk, Vely Zajec
Color and Materials: Yana Khudyakova

Executive Architect: Davis Partnership, Denver,
Colorado (Administration/Cafeteria Facilities)
HLW International, Santa Monica (Process Engineering
/Analytical Laboratory/Offices)
Landscape Architect: Civitas
Photographer: Ron Pollard

MIT SLOAN SCHOOL OF MANAGEMENT
Massachusetts Institute of Technology, Cambridge

Client: Massachusetts Institute of Technology
Design Architect: Moore Ruble Yudell Architects & Planners
Partner-in-Charge: Buzz Yudell
Collaborating Partner: John Ruble
Principal-in-Charge: Neal Matsuno
Principal: Jeanne Chen
Color and Materials: Tina Beebe, Kaoru Orime
Interior Design: Stanley Anderson
Project Team: Wing-Hon Ng, Bob Dolbinski, David
Cutler, Andrew Kao, Heather Hunt, Laurie Groehler
Models: Mark Grand, Ben Foster, Mike Heise, Kentaro
Yamada
Renderer: Al Forster

Associate Architect: Bruner/Cott & Associates, Inc.
Partner-in-Charge: Lee Cott
Principal-in-Charge: Lynne Brooks

LAW-BUSINESS CONNECTION
University of California, Berkeley

Client: University of California, Berkeley
Design Architect: Moore Ruble Yudell Architects & Planners
Partner-in-Charge: Buzz Yudell
Collaborating Partner: John Ruble
Principal-in-Charge: Krista Becker
Principal, Design Lead: Mario Violich
Assistant Project Manager: Richard Destin
Project Coordinator: JT Theeuwes
Associate: Erin Hillhouse, Adam Padua
Interior Design: Stanley Anderson, Kinneret Atia,
Charlotte Thomas, Amy Sklar, Philippe Arias

Exterior Color and Materials: Tina Beebe, Kaoru Orime
Project Team: Oscar Pineda, Simone Barth, Bernardo Frias,
Takuji Mukaiyama, Darin Morris, Kyung-Sun Lee
Models: Benjamin Foster, Mark Grand, Kentaro Yamada,
Michael Heise, Anton Henning, Matthew MacDonald,
Toru Narita, Amy Newborn, Alexander Martinson

Renderer: Al Forster
Landscape Architect: Olin Partnership
Lighting: Horton Lees Brogden

GLORYA KAUFMAN HALL
University of California, Los Angeles

Client: University of California, Los Angeles
Architect: Moore Ruble Yudell Architects & Planners
Partner-in-Charge: Buzz Yudell
Collaborating Partner: John Ruble
Principal-in-Charge: Neal Matsuno
Color and Materials: Tina Beebe
Project Architects: Erin Hillhouse and Marc Schoeplein
Project Team: Martin Saavedra, Angel Gabriel, Roger
Lopez, Matthew Blake, Ted Kane, Laurian Pokroy, Murat
Sanal, Kaoru Orime and Yana Khudyakova
Models: Mark Grand, Don Hornbeck and Joshua Lunn

Theater Consultant: Theatre Projects Consultants—
David Rosenburg, Brian Hall and Michael Nishball
Historic Preservation Consultant: Kaplan Chen
Renderer: Elaine Libbey
Photographer: Tim Griffith, John Edward Linden

DONG HWA UNIVERSITY MASTER PLAN
Hwa-Lien, Taiwan

Client: Planning Office of National Dong Hwa University in
Hualien, Dr. Paul Tzung-Tsann Mu, President
Design Architect: Moore Ruble Yudell Architects & Planners
Principal-in-Charge: John Ruble
Principals: Buzz Yudell, Charles Moore
Associate-in-Charge: Akai Ming-Kae Yang
Project Architect: Ying-Chao Kuo
Project Team: George Nakatani, Marc Peacor
Model makers: Craig Currie, Mark Grand
Renderings: George Nakatani

Associate Architect: LAI Associates
Landscape Architect: Pamela Burton & Company

606 BROADWAY HOUSING
Santa Monica, California

Client: JSM Construction, Inc.
Design Architect: Moore Ruble Yudell Architects & Planners
Partner-in-Charge: Buzz Yudell
Collaborating Partner: John Ruble
Principal-in-Charge: James Mary O'Connor
Principal/Project Manager: Krista Becker
Color and Materials: Tina Beene, Kaoru Orime

Project Team: Kyung-Sun Lee, Tony Tran, Halil Dolan
Digital Renderings: Nozomu Sugawara

Landscape: Pamela Burton & Associates
Executive Architects: DE Architects, Don E. Empakeris, Principal
Models: Model Concepts, Inc.
Photographer: Del Zoppo Productions

FAVORVIEW PALACE EAST DISTRICT
Guangzhou, People's Republic of China

Client: Kingold Group/Kingold Real Estate Development Co.
Design Architect: Moore Ruble Yudell Architects & Planners
Partners: John Ruble, Buzz Yudell
Principal-in-Charge: James Mary O'Connor
Project Team: Halil Dolan, Pooja Bhagat, Kaoru Orime, Tony Tran, Nozomu Sugawara, Takuji Mukaiyama, Toru Narita
Models: Mark Grand, Michael Heise, Benjamin Foster

Landscape Architect: ah'bé Landscape Architects
Principal-in-Charge: Calvin Abe
Associate-in-Charge: Evan Mather
Project Team: Kiku Kurahashi, Annie Pai
Digital Renderings: Josh Ashcroft

NEI-HU RESIDENTIAL TOWERS
Taipei, Taiwan

Client: Win Sing Development Corporation Ltd.
Design Architect: Moore Ruble Yudell Architects & Planners
Partners: John Ruble, Buzz Yudell
Principal-in-Charge: James Mary O'Connor
Project Team: Pooja Bhagat, Halil Dolan, Christopher Jonick, Kaoru Orime, Tony Tran, Takuji Mukaiyama, Toru Narita
Models: Toru Narita, Benjamin Foster, Kentaro Yamada, Michael Heise

Associate Executive Architect: LKP Design, Taipei
Design Principal: Hung-Tsung Ko
Chief Engineer: E. J. Lu
Project Manager: Ya-Ting Chang
Project Team: John-Son Mo, Associate
Andrew Liang, Job Captain/Senior Designer
Jing-Ru Wang, Senior Designer
Chia-Wen Yang, Senior Designer

WATERMARK TOWER
San Francisco, California

Client: Lend Lease Development
Design Architect: Moore Ruble Yudell Architects & Planners
Partner-in-Charge: John Ruble
Collaborating Partner: Buzz Yudell
Associate-in-Charge: Michael de Villiers
Project Team: Joan Young

Color & Materials: Kaoru Orime

Executive Architect: Kwan Henmi Architecture/Planning
Photographer: David Wakely

REGATTA WHARF HOUSING AT JACKSON'S LANDING
Pyrmont, Sydney, Australia

Client: Lend Lease Development
Design Architect: Moore Ruble Yudell Architects & Planners
Partner-in-Charge: John Ruble
Collaborating Partner: Buzz Yudell
Associate-in-Charge: Michael de Villiers
Color and Materials: Tina Beebe, Kaoru Orime
Project Team Phase I: Erin Hillhouse, Alberto Reano, Murat Sanal, Stephen Penhoet, Roger Lopez, Tony Tran, David Ellien
Project Team Phase II: Edgar Diamante, Roger Lopez, Vely Zajec, Tony Tran, Ross Morishige
Models: Mark Grand
Renderers: Al Forster, Ian Espinoza
Associate Architect: Travis McEwen Group, North Sydney, Australia
Photographer: Werner Huthmacher

FAIRMONT HOTEL ADDITION
San Jose, California

Client: Maritz Wolff
Principal: Phillip Maritz, Lew Wolff
VP Construction: Bruce Snow
Design Architect: Moore Ruble Yudell Architects & Planners
Partner-in-Charge: Buzz Yudell
Collaborating Partner: John Ruble.
Principal-in-Charge: James Mary O'Connor
Color and Materials: Tina Beebe, Kaoru Orime
Project Team: Lisa Belian, Tony Tran, Roger Lopez, Izzet Motola

Co-Design Architect/Executive Architect: Gensler Associates
Principal-in-Charge: Andy Cohen
Design Principal: Kevin Hart
Project Manager: Scott Kaufman
Project Architect: Satoru Kato
Construction Project Architect: Frank Chlad
Project Team: Jung Suh, Michael Shurtleff, Jim LeFevre
Digital Renderings: Jung Suh
Interior Design: Wilson & Associates

BEIJING CENTURY CENTER
Beijing, People's Republic of China

Design Architect: Moore Ruble Yudell Architects & Planners
Partners: John Ruble, Buzz Yudell
Principal-in-Charge: James Mary O'Connor
Color and Materials: Tina Beebe, Kaoru Orime
Project Team: Halil Dolan, Tony Tran, Alberto Reano, Angel Gabriel, Bill Ferehawk, Isabel Stomm, Kaoru Orime,

Vely Zajec, Yana Khudyakova, Ed Diamante, Richard Destin, Chris Hamilton, Kyung-Sun Lee
Models: Mark Grand, Alex Solbes, Haruyuki Yokoyama
Research: Rebecca Bubenas, Janet Sager
Digital Illustrator: Craig Shimahara Illustration
Translator: Kathy Cheng

Associate Architect: Yang Architects
Principal-in-Charge: Akai Ming-Kae Yang
Project Liaison: Huntec Development
Principal-in-Charge: Michael Ho
Presentation Model: Model Concepts
Model Photographer: Jim Simmons

SERENDRA MASTER PLAN & RESIDENTIAL/RETAIL
Manila, Philippines

Client: Ayala Land, Inc.
Design Architect: Moore Ruble Yudell Architects & Planners
Partners: John Ruble, Buzz Yudell
Principal-in-Charge: James Mary O'Connor
Principal: Krista Becker
Color and Materials: Tina Beebe, Kaoru Orime, Yana Khudyakova
Project Team: Peter Sjöström, Kyung-Sun Lee, David Cutler, Christian Robert, Tony Tran, Tim Feigenbutz, Halil Dolan
Models: John Leimbach, Veronica Vela, Mark Grand, Carissa Shrock

Landscape Architect: Mia Lehrer + Associates
Principal-in-Charge: Mia Lehrer
Project Team: Holly Kuwayama, Patricia Akinaga, Louisa Relia
Design Managers: Innovation and Design Group, Ayala Land, Inc. (Angie Lacson)
Consulting Architect: LVLP Architects (Leandro Y Locsin, Jr.)
Associate Architects: High End Buildings: GF & Partners (Ted Narciso)
Core-Mid Buildings: LVLP, RMJM Philippines, Inc. (Abelardo M. Tolentino, Jr.)

RESORT DEVELOPMENT
Southeast China

Design Architect: Moore Ruble Yudell Architects & Planners
Partners: John Ruble, Buzz Yudell
Principal-in-Charge: James Mary O'Connor
Project Team: Halil Dolan, Pooja Bhagat, Kaoru Orime, Tony Tran, Takuji Mukaiyama, Toru Narita, Kentaro Yamada, Nozomu Sugawara
Models: Kentaro Yamada, Benjamin Foster

Landscape Architect: ah'bé Landscape Architects
Principal-in-Charge: Calvin Abe
Associate Architects (competition): andrew lee king fun & associates architects limited
Associate Architects: Archiplus International Limited
Digital Renderings: Shimahara Illustration

Landscape concept sketches: Calvin Abe
Renderings: Tony Tran
Presentation Model: Model Concepts
Model Photographer: Jim Simmons

CHUN SEN BI AN MASTER PLAN & HOUSING
Chongqing, People's Republic of China

Client: Longhu Real Estate Development Inc.
Design Architect: Moore Ruble Yudell Architects & Planners
Partners: John Ruble, Buzz Yudell
Principal-in-Charge: James Mary O'Connor
Color and Materials: Tina Beebe, Kaoru Orime
Project Team: Halil Dolan, Pooja Bhagat, Kyung-Sun Lee, Chris Jonick, Peter Sjöström, Tony Tran, Simone Barth, Nozomu Sugawara, Clay Holden, Therese Kelly
Models: Mark Grand, Sang Lee, Takuji Mukaiyama, Philippe Arias, Kirk Soderstrom, Nicholas Worden, Joel Chappo

Associate Architect: Yang Architects;
Principal-in-Charge: Akai Ming-Kae Yang
Project Team: Ning Lin, Kristina Hahn, Nicolas Rousset, Qi Li, Juan Chen, Chi-Hsuan Tsai, Xiao-Yan Sun, Chung-Cheng Li, Rayna Rong Fan, Lin-Qi Mei, Eric Chen, Matias Creimer, Xu Xi, Soyeon Choi, Zhongkai Chen, Alice Yao
Models: Alfredo Gonzales
Landscape Architect: Burton & Company
(Competition Phase)
Digital Renderings: Craig Shimahara Illustration

PHOTOGRAPHY CREDITS

Images by: BrubakerPhotography.com: 106 bottom left and center
Art Gray: 50, 54, 57, 130 center, 134, 246
Tim Griffith: 9 top left, 84, 87–91, 92 top left and right, 93, 160, 161 top right, 162 top right, 163, 246 center
Tim Hursley: 243, 244
Werner Huthmacher: 9 top right, 32, 34–36, 38–39, 41–43, 52–53, 55–56, 58–59, 62–64, 65 top right, 66–67, 110, 112–113, 114 left, 194, 197–199, 244 center, 245 right
Ole Jais: 37
Alan Karchmer: 7 top left, 10, 114 right, 115, 116, 119–121, 123 left, 124–125, 130 left, 132–133, 135
John Edward Linden: 9 top center, 11, 94, 96 top, 97 bottom left, 98–103, 126, 128–129, 130 right, 131, 158, 162 top left
Jim McHugh: 236, 237 top left, 238 top left and right, 239 top left
Lars Mongs: 60, 244
Anna Valentina Murch and Douglas Hollis: 92 bottom
Ron Pollard: 122, 144, 146–148, 149 bottom
Jim Simmons: 8 top center, 152 top, 172, 174–176, 180, 218, 232–233
David Wakely: 190, 192–193
Kim Zwarts: 20, 22–26, 28–31, 245 center

All other photography courtesy of Moore Ruble Yudell Architects & Planners

ACKNOWLEDGMENTS

We are indebted to Bruce Lan, Project Director at AADCU, for this significant opportunity to present our recent work to a larger audience in Asia. It is a pleasure and honor to be included in AADCU's series of reports on Contemporary Architects in the United States.

We wish to thank Frances Anderton for her thought-provoking questions and keen perspective on our work. We are grateful to Robert Campbell for his continued support of our work, and for the further use of his essay, which is provided by permission of Paul Latham and Images Publishing.

Ken Kim provided both the very fine graphic design and many ideas in the development of the structure and message of this monograph. He was assisted by Rebecca Bubenas, Tony Tran, Kaoru Orime, and Rachael Howard. Heather Hunt also supported us in assisting with translation.

Any presentation of built work depends entirely on photography, and we are fortunate to have a number of diverse talents represented in this work, including Werner Huthmacher, Kim Zwarts, Alan Karchmer, Tim Griffith, John Edward Linden, Ron Pollard, Art Gray, Tim Hursley, Jim Simmons, Ole Jais, David Wakely, Lee Brubaker, and Lars Mongs. In addition, our work has been visualized by extraordinary illustrators and artists, such as Craig Shimahara, Doug Jamieson, and Al Forster, as well as model makers Bijan Fahimian and Mark Grand.

As we test bringing our humanistic approach to the design of architecture at larger scales in near and far away places, we would also like to thank the continued support of our clients and colleagues in making the work in this book possible. Shouzhi Wang, who has also contributed his own writing in this volume, has been a trusted friend, ally, and guide during some of our most important advances in working in China. Similarly Akai Ming-Kae Yang, our partner for Chen Sen Bi An, has helped us find our way.

Within the office, we also wish to thank Halil Dolan, Takuji Mukaiyama, Toru Norita, Nozomu Sugawara, and Pooja Bhagat, for their part in creating this monograph, and many of the recent works it presents.

As we look into the future, we are certain to benefit from the energy, talent, and commitment of our diverse, international team of partners and colleagues.

John Ruble, Buzz Yudell, James Mary O'Connor

图书在版编目（CIP）数据

摩尔　乐伯　约德／美国亚洲艺术与设计协作联盟（AADCU）主编.
－沈阳：辽宁科学技术出版社，2007.3
ISBN 978-7-5381-4946-3
I. 摩…II. 美…III. 建筑设计—作品集—美国—现代　IV. TU206
中国版本图书馆 CIP 数据核字（2007）第 002713 号

出版发行：辽宁科学技术出版社
　　　　　（地址：沈阳市和平区十一纬路 25 号 邮编：110003）
印　刷　者：广州一丰印刷有限公司
经　销　者：各地新华书店
幅面尺寸：290mm X 250mm
印　　　张：21
字　　　数：90 千字
插　　　页：4
出版时间：2007 年 3 月第一版
印刷时间：2007 年 3 月第一次印刷
责任编辑：符宁　郭健　闻通
责任校对：徐跃

定版发价：280. 00 元
联系电话：024－23284536
邮购热线：024－23284502
E－mail：tad4356@mail.lnpgc.com.cn
http：//www.lnkj.com.cn